REVISE FC

NEAB

MODULAR

science

NIGEL ENGLISH

Heinemann

FOUNDATION

Heinemann Educational Publishers
Halley Court, Jordan Hill, Oxford, OX2 8EJ
a division of Reed Educational & Professional Publishing Ltd

Heinemann is a registered trademark of Reed Educational &
Professional Publishing Ltd.

OXFORD   MELBOURNE   AUCKLAND
JOHANNESBURG   BLANTYRE   GABORONE
IBADAN   PORTSMOUTH (NH) USA   CHICAGO

First published 1997

ISBN 0 435 10163 3

01 00
10 9 8 7 6 5

Edited on-screen by Sarah Ware

Designed and typeset by Ken Vail Graphic Design

Illustrated by Graeme Morris (Ken Vail Graphic Design)

Cover design by Threefold Design

Cover artwork by Stephen May

Printed and bound in Great Britain by The Bath Press

Acknowledgements
The authors and publishers would like to thank the following for
permission to use photographs:
page 1: Tony Stone, *page 20 top*: Pictor, *bottom*: Nigel English,
page 41: Sygma, *page 85*: Tony Stone

The publishers have made every effort to trace the copyright
holders, but if they have inadvertently overlooked any, they will be
pleased to make the necessary arrangements at the first opportunity.

Picture research by Natalie Stewart

From the author
I would particularly like to thank my family, Chris, Philip and
Katharine, for their help and forbearance in writing this book.

Contents

★ against a module denotes it is a module assessed by terminal examination.

How to use this book

The revision guide contains the 12 modules which form the NEAB Modular Science scheme. They cover the Foundation Tier of the syllabus.

You will need to learn and understand these six modules for module tests during the course:

AT2	**AT3**	**AT4**
Humans as Organisms	*Metals*	*Energy*
Maintenance of Life	*Earth Materials*	*Electricity*

You will need to learn and understand these six modules for the terminal exam:

AT2	**AT3**	**AT4**
Environment	*Patterns of Chemical Change*	*Forces*
Inheritance and Selection	*Structures and Bonding*	*Waves and Radiation*

You will also have to revise certain areas of the first group of six modules above for the terminal exam. These are very clearly marked by a vertical black line in the margin of the text, as shown here.

As you approach a module test or the terminal exam in your course, you can organise your work like this.

> Work through the module or modules you need. Pace yourself – do one double page spread at a time and look back at the notes you have made in class on this topic.

> Try the questions at the end of every double page spread to check that you really understand the topic.

> Check your answers under *Answers to end of spread questions* (page 142). Go back over anything you find difficult.

> Do the test style questions at the end of each module. These are in the same style as the questions you will have to do in the real end of module test or terminal exam, so they are very good practice.

> Check your answers against the *Answers to module tests and terminal exam questions* (page 132). In terminal exam style questions take care to cover all the points needed to get full marks. Go back over areas you find difficult.

When you are revising for the terminal exams you will also need to revise the material marked with a vertical black line in the other six modules. Revise these alongside modules in the same AT. For example, as you work through *Structures and Bonding* or *Patterns of Chemical Change* in AT3 it would be a good idea to revise the terminal exam material in *Metals* or *Earth Materials* at the same time.

The words in **bold** are all key words you need to know. A useful revision idea would be to build up your own glossary of these as you work through the book. For quick reference to a word or topic use the *Index* at the back of the book.

AT2

Life Processes and Living Things

Humans as Organisms

Maintenance of Life

Environment

Inheritance and Selection

Life processes

How do animals and plants differ from non-living things?

They all have the following:

- **M**ovement – it is clear that animals move, but plants move as well (e.g. they grow towards the light)
- **R**espiration – they use oxygen to release energy from food
- **S**ensitivity – they react to their surroundings (e.g. by using hearing, smell or sight)
- **G**rowth – all animals and plants start as a single cell and most become complex organisms with millions of cells
- **R**eproduction – they produce more of their own type
- **E**xcretion – they get rid of the waste products they produce
- **N**utrition – plants make their own food, animals eat plants or other animals.

Checkpoint

Cover the list of life processes, then write them down. Use **MRS GREN** to help you remember. Check your answer.

Cells

What makes up animals and plants?

They are made up from cells. All animal cells have:

- a **nucleus** – this controls everything a cell does
- **cytoplasm** – this is the liquid where the cell's chemical reactions take place
- a **cell membrane** which allows substances into and out of the cell.

We are not just made up of lots of disorganised cells. Cells are **specialised** to carry out different jobs (**functions**) within the body.

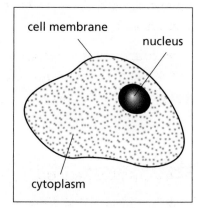

A typical animal cell

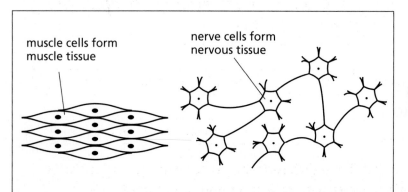

Types of tissue

Just think!

You started out as one cell. When you are fully grown you will have 5 or 6 billion cells!

Cells make up **tissues**, and different tissues make up **organs**. A group of organs forms a **system**.

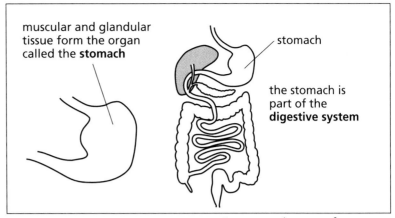

muscular and glandular tissue form the organ called the **stomach**

stomach

the stomach is part of the **digestive system**

An organ is part of a system

Nutrition

People need three main types of food: proteins, carbohydrates and fats.

Carbohydrates provide energy. We get them from foods such as cereals (e.g. bread, pasta, cornflakes), fruit and root vegetables (e.g. potatoes and carrots).

Fats provide energy as well. The body also needs fats to make cell membranes. We get fats from milk, cheese, butter and margarine.

Proteins are used for growth and for replacing damaged cells. We get them from meat, fish, eggs and pulses (e.g. beans and peas).

 Questions

1   Most of the life processes are taking place in your body right now. List those which are happening in you at this moment, and those which are not.

2   Draw a table for the different foodstuffs (like the table shown here). Use the information on this page to fill in the gaps.

Type of food	Used for	Found in
	growth and replacing cells	meat, fish, eggs and pulses (e.g. peas)
	energy	
fats		milk, cheese, butter and margarine

3   Muscle cells and gland cells have different shapes to help them in the jobs they do, but they have *three* structures in common. What are they?

Eating and digestion

Food has to get to the cells of the body so that they have the energy they need.

To do this food has to be **digested**. This means that your body breaks it down from the large, insoluble lumps which you eat into small, soluble particles. These small particles can then move into the blood, which transports them to the body cells.

This breakdown happens in the **digestive system**.

The digestive system

This has a number of organs including the gullet, stomach, liver, pancreas, small intestine and large intestine.

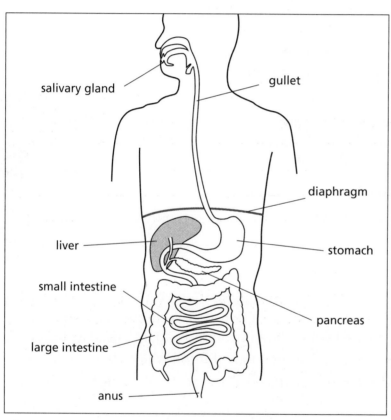

The human digestive system

How it works

When you eat a meal, this is what happens.

- Muscles in the wall of the gullet, stomach and intestines move the food along.
- **Glands** produce **enzymes** which help to speed up the digestion (breakdown) of the food.

 **Just think!**

Your food travels through 10 metres of gut and takes 24–48 hours to digest fully!

- The salivary glands (in the mouth), pancreas and small intestine produce **carbohydrase**. This speeds up the breakdown of carbohydrates into sugars.

- The stomach, pancreas and small intestine produce **protease** enzymes. These speed up the breakdown of proteins into amino acids.

- The pancreas and small intestine produce **lipase** enzymes. These speed up the breakdown of fats into fatty acids and glycerol.

The stomach also produces hydrochloric acid to kill most of the bacteria taken in with the food. The enzymes in the stomach work best in these acid conditions.

The body cannot digest some food, so this goes on into the large intestine. The large intestine absorbs most of the water from the food back into the body. The undigested food then passes out of the body through the anus as faeces.

Help

- CARBOHYDrases break down CARBOHYDrates.
- PROTEases break down PROTEins.
- LIPases break down fats (LIPids).

Questions

1   Copy out this table and fill in the gaps:

Name of organ	Enzymes it produces
salivary glands	
stomach	
pancreas	
small intestine	

2   A cheese sandwich has carbohydrate (bread), fat (butter) and protein (cheese). This flow chart shows how the carbohydrate is broken down in the digestive system:

carbohydrate in bread
↓
carbohydrase in mouth, pancreas and small intestine
↓
sugars in blood

Draw similar flow charts for the digestion of the fat and protein from the sandwich.

3   If someone has diarrhoea, their faeces is loose and watery. Why does this suggest that something may be wrong with their large intestine?

Breathing and respiration

Respiration

Why do we need to breathe? Don't just answer 'to stay alive'!

We breathe to take in oxygen from the air. Our body cells use the oxygen to release energy from food broken down in the digestive system. The food used is glucose, a type of sugar.

This is called **respiration**. Because it uses oxygen, it is called **aerobic** respiration.

Body cells produce carbon dioxide when they respire. We need to breathe out this gas. Carbon dioxide is a waste product of respiration. Water is also a waste product.

So respiration is:

$$\text{glucose} + \text{oxygen} \rightarrow \text{carbon dioxide} + \text{water} + \text{energy}$$

Sometimes, if there is a shortage of oxygen, body cells can respire **anaerobically** (that is, without oxygen) to produce the energy they need. The waste product from this is lactic acid, which quickly makes the muscles feel tired, so your body can't keep up anaerobic respiration for long!

Why do we need energy?

We use the energy from food to:

- make our muscles contract so that we can move
- keep us warm when our surroundings are colder than we are – our body temperature needs to be kept the same all the time
- build up large, useful substances from the small, digested ones we take into our blood. We then use these substances to grow and to repair our bodies if they are damaged.

The breathing system

Oxygen passes into our blood through the lungs, and carbon dioxide passes out through the lungs.

The lungs are in the top part of your body (the **thorax**). They are separated from organs such as the stomach in the lower half of your body (the **abdomen**) by the **diaphragm**. The lungs are protected by a cage of bones called the **ribs**.

 **Checkpoint**

Cover the page, then write down the *two* things cells need for respiration and the *three* things they produce. Check your answer.

 **Just think!**

If you are 16 years old, you have breathed in and out about 75 million times in your life! Each time, you have taken in oxygen and got rid of waste carbon dioxide.

Diffusion

The gases (oxygen or carbon dioxide) pass between the lungs and the blood through the **alveoli** in the lungs. These are millions of tiny air sacs with very thin walls. They are surrounded by lots of tiny blood vessels.

The gases **diffuse** through these thin walls. This means that they pass from the side where they are more concentrated to the side where they are less concentrated. When the oxygen in the blood reaches other cells in the body it enters the cells by **diffusion** through the cell membranes.

When you breathe in, the air in the alveoli has more oxygen than the blood – so oxygen diffuses into the blood. When it reaches the lungs, the blood has more carbon dioxide than the alveoli – so carbon dioxide diffuses into the alveoli.

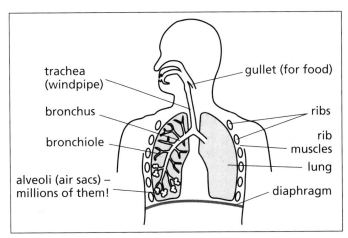

The breathing system

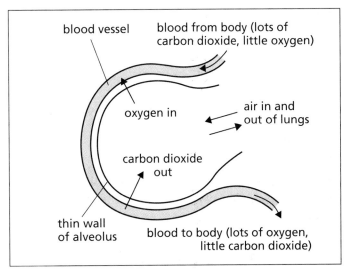

Gas exchange in the alveoli

 Questions

1   Copy and complete the sentences, choosing words from this list:

   water   oxygen   breathe   carbon dioxide   energy   glucose   respire

   Our cells use _____ from the air to _____. This produces _____ and the waste products are _____ and _____.

2   Our lungs are very delicate and important organs. Look at the diagram again. What protects the lungs from being crushed and damaged from outside?

3   Some types of exercise are called 'aerobic'. Suggest benefits to the body of aerobic exercise.

The circulatory system

This is really the body's transport system, with blood carrying substances around.

What is blood?

Blood consists of a liquid called **plasma** which carries red cells, white cells and platelets. Plasma also carries:

- carbon dioxide from the cells to the lungs
- digested food from the small intestine to the cells and organs of the body
- urea from the liver to the kidneys.

Red blood cells carry oxygen for respiration from the lungs to all the body organs.

Red cells are full of **haemoglobin**. They don't have a nucleus. When a red cell picks up oxygen in the lungs the haemoglobin becomes **oxy-haemoglobin**. When it gives up oxygen to other cells in the body, oxy-haemoglobin becomes haemoglobin.

White cells help defend the body against microbes (e.g. bacteria) that may cause disease. They have a nucleus.

Platelets are bits of cells. They don't have a nucleus. When the skin is cut they help to form blood clots (these are the scabs which form over the cuts).

The circulation system

We actually have two separate circulation systems – one to the lungs and one to the rest of the body.

The heart is a powerful muscle pumping blood around the body. It is divided into four parts or chambers. When blood enters the heart it goes into an **atrium**. The atrium contracts and squeezes the blood through into a **ventricle**. The ventricle contracts and forces the blood out of the heart.

Valves in the heart make the blood flow in the right direction. They stop the blood flowing backwards.

 *Checkpoint*

Cover the page then write down what white cells and platelets do.
Check your answer.

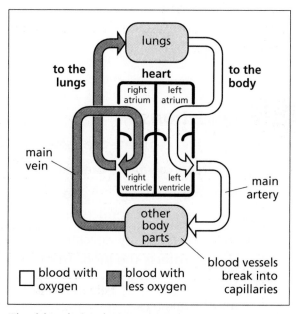

The blood circulation system

The blood vessels

Arteries are large vessels which carry blood away from the heart. The heart pumps out blood with great force and arteries have thick, muscular, elastic walls to cope with this high pressure.

Veins are also large vessels which bring blood back to the heart. The pressure from the heartbeat is low by the time the blood gets to the veins, so they have thinner walls than arteries. They also have valves along their length to prevent the backflow of blood, especially when it is coming back from your feet!

Capillaries are very narrow, thin-walled blood vessels which run through the organs of the body. Blood flows into them from the arteries and out to the veins.

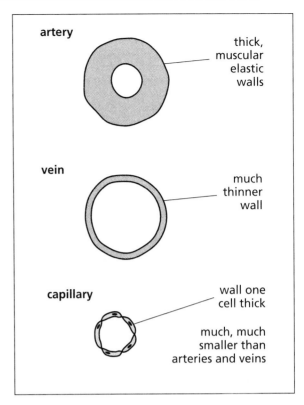

The thin walls allow substances to get in and out of the capillaries. For example, oxygen and glucose go from the capillaries to the body cells, and carbon dioxide and water come from the body cells to the blood.

This happens by diffusion (like the movement of gases through the alveoli in the lungs). When water, sugar and other nutrients are more concentrated in the blood than in the cells, they pass through the cell membrane into the cell. The greater the difference in concentration, the faster diffusion happens.

 Just think!

When you feel your pulse it is an artery getting wider as blood surges through.

 Help

Only gases or substances dissolved in water can diffuse through cell membranes.

 Question

1　Copy this table and fill in the gaps.

Parts of the blood	What they do	Structure
plasma		liquid
red cells		no nucleus, contains haemoglobin
white cells		
	help heal cuts	

Disease

What causes disease? One of the main causes is when **microbes** such as certain bacteria and viruses get into the body. These cause a whole range of illnesses, from the common cold to meningitis and AIDS.

Microbes

Bacterial cells have cytoplasm surrounded by a cell membrane. All of this is surrounded by a cell wall. They have no nucleus. Usually, the genes which allow a cell to reproduce and make copies of itself are in its nucleus. In bacteria, the genes are in the cytoplasm.

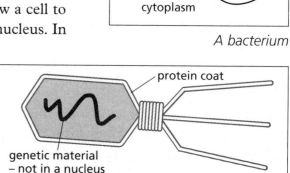

A bacterium

Viruses are much smaller than bacteria. They are very different from cells. They have a protein coat surrounding a few genes. They can reproduce only inside the living cells of organisms.

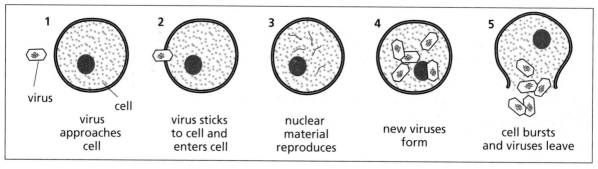

A virus

If large numbers of microbes (bacteria or viruses) enter your body then you may catch a disease. The microbes can reproduce very quickly inside your body so that there are soon millions of them. They may produce poisons (also called **toxins**) which make you feel ill.

If a virus reproduces in one of your cells, the cell will be damaged.

A virus reproducing

Defence against disease

The best way is to stop the bugs (microbes) getting in! Your body can do this in several ways.

- Skin acts as protection – if you have a cut, microbes can get straight through into your blood.

- Blood clots and forms scabs, which seal cuts in the skin and stop microbes getting in.

- Air passages in your nose and lungs have thick, sticky mucus on their surfaces inside to trap microbes – when you blow your nose or cough you are getting rid of these trapped microbes.

- Your stomach contains acid which can kill most microbes.

But if the microbes manage to get in then white cells spring into action. They:

- ingest (eat) the bacteria
- produce **antibodies** which help destroy particular bacteria or viruses
- produce **antitoxins** to neutralise (get rid of) the poisons (toxins).

If your body is infected with a particular microbe, the white cells produce particular antibodies to fight it. The next time that microbe invades your body, the white cells can produce the right antibodies much more quickly – your body is now **immune** to the infection.

this white cell surrounds and ingests bacteria

this white cell produces antibodies

White blood cells attack invading microbes

Disease and lifestyle

How do you come into contact with harmful microbes?

Here are two ways.

- When ill people cough or sneeze they release a fine spray which contains microbes. If you breathe these in you risk catching the same illness.

- If you eat food prepared in unhygienic conditions or drink unclean water, you may become ill. Unclean water is often found when large numbers of people are crowded into one place without any sewage treatment systems. It can carry the killer disease cholera which spreads very fast.

Questions

1   Draw a spider diagram to show all the defences the human body has against microbes. Put **the body** at the centre of the diagram.

2   A bacterial cell has *two* things which are different from an ordinary animal cell. What are they?

3   'Coughs and sneezes spread diseases.' Why?

Module test questions

1   The table is about some of the processes of life.
Match words from the list with each of the numbers **1–4** in the table.

respire
excrete
respond
reproduce

	Definition
1	produce more of the same kind
2	release energy from food
3	remove waste products from the body
4	react with the surroundings

2   These sentences are about the blood system.
Choose words from the list for each of the spaces **1–4** in the sentences.

white cells
platelets
plasma
red cells

Oxygen is carried by ____**1**____ in the blood. The liquid part of the blood is called ____**2**____. Normally the skin keeps microbes out, but if the skin is cut ____**3**____ help to form blood clots. If microbes do get into the blood then ____**4**____ help defend the body.

3   The diagram shows part of the breathing system.
Choose words from the list for each of the labels **1–4** on the diagram.

bronchus
trachea
rib
air sac

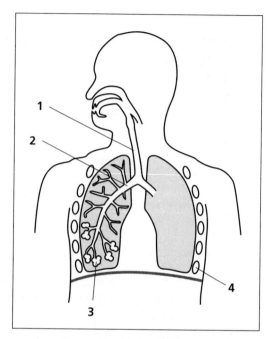

4   These sentences are about the types of food that we eat.
Choose words from the list for each of the spaces **1–4** in the sentences.
You will have to use one of the words more than once.

carbohydrate
fat
protein

Cheese is a good source of ____**1**____ which is used to help make cell membranes.
____**2**____ is found in meat and is used for growth.
Cereals are a good source of ____**3**____ which is used to provide energy.
We need to replace cells all of the time – ____**4**____ is the food in our diet which helps us do this.

5 Which *two* of the following statements are true about the stomach?

   A it produces lipase enzymes

   B digested food is absorbed through its walls

   C the conditions inside it are acid

   D it produces carbohydrase and protease enzymes

   E it produces protease enzymes.

6 Which *two* of the following statements are true about the circulation system?

   A it transports carbon dioxide from the organs to the lungs

   B it transports oxygen from the organs to the lungs

   C it transports urea from the kidneys to the liver

   D it transports digested food from the small intestine to the organs

   E it transports digested food from the organs to the small intestine.

7 This is a diagram of the circulatory system.

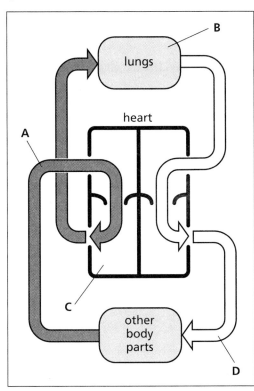

1. In which part of the system is oxygen picked up?

   A B C D

2. Which part of the system pumps deoxygenated blood?

   A B C D

3. Which part of the system carries oxygenated blood to the body?

   A B C D

4. Which part of the system is carrying blood at low pressure back to the heart?

   A B C D

8 This question is about respiration.

1. What are the two waste products of respiration?

   A oxygen and water

   B carbon dioxide and water

   C oxygen and carbon dioxide

   D carbon dioxide and nitrogen.

2. Which best describes respiration?

   A the release of energy from food

   B the release of energy from oxygen

   C the exchange of gases

   D the breathing in of oxygen and out of carbon dioxide.

3. The proper name for an air sac in the lungs is:

   A bronchus

   B bronchiole

   C larynx

   D alveolus.

4. Which of the following is *not* an adaptation of the lungs which helps gas exchange?

   A good blood supply

   B dry surfaces

   C large surface area

   D thin walls.

How do plants make their food?

Plant and animal cells

Plant and animal cells are made up from different parts. They have some parts in common:

- a **nucleus** – controlling what the cell does
- **cytoplasm** – liquid where cell reactions take place
- **cell membrane** – allowing substances in and out of the cell (e.g. oxygen).

Plant cells have three parts which animal cells never have:

- **cell wall** – so that the cell stays the same rigid shape
- **chloroplasts** – which absorb energy from light to make food for the plant
- a **vacuole** – which contains a liquid called the cell sap.

Checkpoint

Cover the page, then write down which three parts all cells have and what they do. Check your answer.

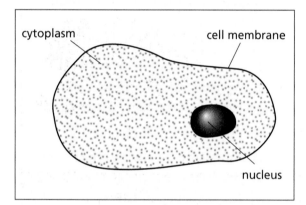

A typical animal cell

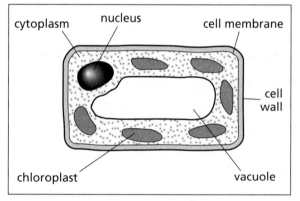

A typical plant cell

Not all of the millions of cells in a plant are the same. Like animals, plants have specialised cells to do certain jobs. For example, **xylem** cells help to transport water around a plant. A group of specialised cells is called a **tissue** (e.g. xylem tissue). Different tissues group together to form an **organ**. A leaf is an example of a plant organ.

Parts of a plant

Flowering plants have:

- **roots** – which hold (anchor) them in the ground
- **stems** – which hold the leaves up to the light and the flowers up so that they can be seen and move water and food around the plant
- **leaves** – which use energy from light to make food.

Making food

Plants make their own food. Animals can't – they have to eat plants or other animals.

Plants make their food by **photosynthesis**. This produces sugar (glucose) for the plant to use. It is done like this:

- green **chlorophyll** in the chloroplasts traps (absorbs) light, which provides energy
- this energy is used to make carbon dioxide and water into sugar
- oxygen is given off as a waste product.

 **Just think!**

Green plants produce their own food – if it wasn't for them we would all be dead!

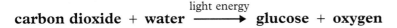

$$\textbf{carbon dioxide} + \textbf{water} \xrightarrow{\text{light energy}} \textbf{glucose} + \textbf{oxygen}$$

Plants usually store the glucose as starch. This is insoluble (it does not dissolve in water). When the plants need the starch for energy (or growth) they change it back into glucose.

What do plants need for photosynthesis?

Plants need:

- carbon dioxide
- some warmth
- water
- light.

Respiration

Plant cells respire just like animal cells. They use some of the glucose made during photosynthesis to release energy.

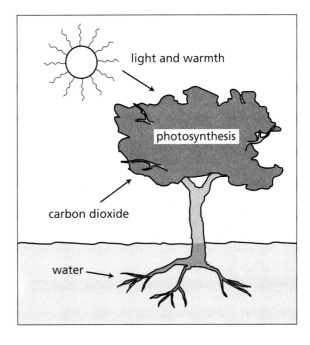

light and warmth

photosynthesis

carbon dioxide

water

 Questions

1   You have lots of cells in your body. There are three structures plant cells have that none of your cells have. What are they and what do they do?

2   This question is about photosynthesis. Copy and complete the sentences, choosing words from this list:

　　carbon dioxide　　oxygen　　chlorophyll　　water　　glucose

　　Plants take in _____ and _____ in order to photosynthesise. The _____ in the leaves traps the Sun's energy. They produce _____ , which they store as starch. The waste gas they produce is called _____ .

3   Why don't people have to cut their lawns in the winter?

Transport in plants

Gases

How do plants get the carbon dioxide they need to photosynthesise?

It enters the leaves through holes called **stomata** (one hole is called a **stoma**). The carbon dioxide diffuses into the leaves and then into the cells (that is, it spreads from a higher concentration to a lower one).

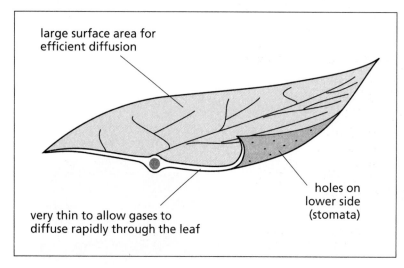

large surface area for efficient diffusion

very thin to allow gases to diffuse rapidly through the leaf

holes on lower side (stomata)

Cross-section through a leaf

Oxygen also moves in and out of the leaves through the stomata.

Taking in water

Plants take in water through their roots. Most of this is absorbed by the **root hair cells**.

Plants also take in mineral salts with the water. These include nitrates which are needed for healthy growth. Flowering plants transport water and nutrients to their stems and leaves through xylem tissue.

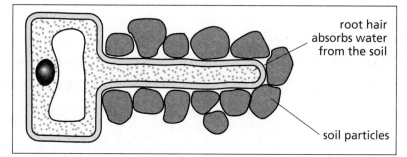

root hair absorbs water from the soil

soil particles

A root hair cell

Losing water

Plants lose water from their leaves because it evaporates through the stomata. This is called **transpiration**. Transpiration happens most on hot, dry and windy days.

If plants lose water faster than their roots can replace it, they **wilt**. This is especially dangerous for young plants, which are mostly held up by water in their cells.

So plants have ways of cutting down the amount of transpiration (water loss):

- most plants have a thick, waxy layer on their leaves to stop them losing too much water (e.g. plants which live in very hot, dry conditions have thicker waxy layers)

- the stomata are surrounded by **guard cells** which control their size. These close if too much water is lost.

Just think!

If it wasn't for water, most small plants would fall over!

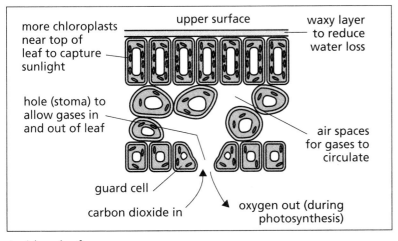

Inside a leaf

Food

The sugars made in the leaves by photosynthesis are transported to the rest of the plant by **phloem** tissue, especially to growing parts or places where the sugar is stored as starch.

Checkpoint

Cover the page, then write down what xylem and phloem transport.
Check your answer.

Questions

1 Copy and complete the sentences, choosing words from this list:

   xylem   sugars   phloem   nutrients   water

   In a plant it is the _____ which transports _____ and _____ from the roots to all parts. Photosynthesis results in the production of _____ which are transported by _____ to all parts of the plant, but particularly to areas where there is a lot of growth.

2 How can a leaf reduce the amount of water it transpires (that is, water that evaporates from its surface)?

How do plants respond?

In other words, how do plants react to their surroundings?

You know that you can respond to things in many ways – but what do plants do? They can respond to light, moisture and to gravity:

- **shoots** grow towards the light and away from the force of gravity

- **roots** grow towards moisture and the force of gravity.

Plant hormones make these things happen. Hormones are chemical messengers. Animals have hormones as well – but they are different to plant hormones.

 **Just think!**

No matter how you plant a seed, the shoot grows up and the roots grow down!

Hormones collect on the lower sides of shoots and roots. In shoots, this makes the lower side grow faster, so the shoot bends up as it grows. In roots the hormones slow down the growth on the lower side, so the root grows down.

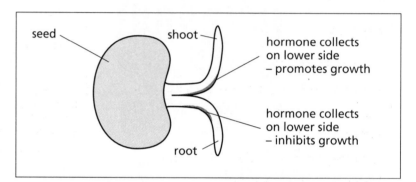

Other plant hormones control growth and reproduction. We use them to:

- help plant cuttings to grow roots and produce large numbers of plants quickly

- ripen fruit at the time the grower wants it to ripen

- kill weeds in the garden by causing them to grow so rapidly that they die.

 **Checkpoint**

Cover the page and write down *three* ways gardeners and growers use plant hormones.
Check your answer.

How do humans respond?

Reacting to our surroundings

We must react in the right way. If you touch a hot pan it is no good scratching your leg! You always make a **coordinated** response.

Changes to our surroundings are called **stimuli** (e.g. looking at a bright light, touching a sharp object). These changes are detected by **receptors** (e.g. the eyes detect the bright light, nerve endings in the skin detect pain).

Just think!

If something is going to hit you, it's no good rubbing your nose!

We can respond to many different stimuli.

Receptors in	are sensitive to	which means
eye	light	you can see
ear	sound	you can hear
ear	changes in position	you can balance
tongue and nose	chemicals	you can taste and smell
skin	pressure and temperature	you can feel heat and different textures

All these receptors send information to your brain. It is your brain that coordinates your response (makes sure that you do the right thing).

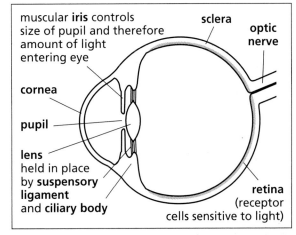

The structure of the eye

The eye

This is how you see:

- light enters the eye through the cornea

- the cornea *and* lens focus light on the retina

- the receptor cells of the retina send messages along the optic nerve to the brain.

The optic nerve is a bundle of **sensory neurones** (nerves). They carry messages in the form of **impulses**.

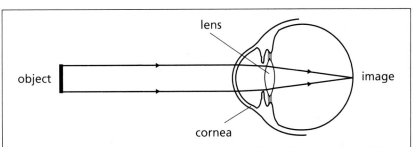

How the eye focuses

Questions

1   The sentences below are about growth in plants. Copy and complete the sentences, choosing words from this list:

downwards   lower   quickly   hormones   upwards   upper   slowly

If a shoot starts growing horizontally from a seed the growth _____ collect on the _____ side. This causes the shoot on that side to grow more _____ and therefore the shoot grows _____ .

2   What is the job of each of these parts of the eye?
    a iris   b retina   c optic nerve   d lens.

Reacting to things inside us

We also react to things happening inside us. This is known as controlling our internal environment.

The body produces substances that it has to get rid of, or **excrete**. These include:

- carbon dioxide – a waste product of respiration, excreted through the lungs
- urea – produced by the liver (from amino acids we don't want) and excreted by the kidneys in the urine, which is stored in the bladder until we can get rid of it.

Hormones

A lot of what happens inside us is controlled by **hormones**. These are chemicals produced by glands and carried by the blood. There are many different hormones with different jobs. Each hormone acts on one particular organ.

Keeping a balance

Some things inside us need to be kept at a constant level. These include water content, ions and temperature.

Water content

We lose water through our lungs when we breathe out and through our skin when we sweat. If we lose too much and the amount of water in our bodies drops too low, we have to take in more by eating and drinking. If we have too much water, our kidneys remove the extra (excess) and it leaves the body in the urine.

Ions

We lose mineral ions (e.g. iron, calcium, sodium) through sweat when we are hot. If we have too many ions our kidneys remove the excess and they leave the body in the urine.

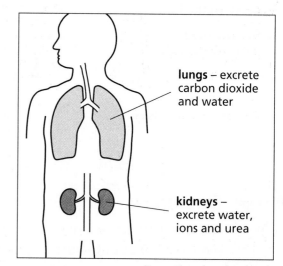

lungs – excrete carbon dioxide and water

kidneys – excrete water, ions and urea

Excretion by the body

Temperature

Our bodies must stay the same temperature inside because our enzymes work best at this temperature. If we get too hot or too cold they won't work and we will die. We lose heat by sweating. On hot days we sweat more so we need to drink more.

Sugar

Sugar is essential to our bodies. It supplies all our body cells with the energy they need. But we must keep the amount of sugar in our blood at the right level. If we have too much or too little it can be fatal.

So how do we keep the amount of sugar at the right level? Two hormones, **insulin** and **glucagon**, control the level. They are both produced by the pancreas. Insulin stops the sugar level rising too high, and glucagon stops it from falling too low.

Sometimes the pancreas does not produce enough insulin and this causes the disease **diabetes**. People with diabetes have to control the sugar in their diet carefully and may have injections of insulin into their blood to control the problem.

Help

When the sugar level in your blood rises too high your pancreas releases insulin. When the sugar level falls too low your pancreas releases glucagon.

Checkpoint

Cover the page. Can you remember what insulin and glucagon do?
Check your answer.

Drugs

There are many different drugs. Some are useful and help cure disease. However, nearly all drugs are dangerous if not used properly. Some drugs are illegal. You need to know about three types.

Solvents such as those found in some glues affect behaviour and may cause damage to the lungs, liver and brain. 	**Tobacco smoke** contains substances which can cause lung cancer, emphysema (lung disease) as well as disease of the heart and blood vessels.	**Alcohol** affects the nervous system by slowing down reactions. It can lead to lack of self control, unconsciousness and coma. It also affects the liver and brain and can permanently damage both. 

Questions

1 Copy and complete the table using these words:

carbon dioxide
water
urea

Substance	Excreted by the
	skin and kidneys
	lungs only
	lungs, skin and kidneys
	kidneys only

2 What happens to the level of sugar in the blood if, during a meal, you eat a lot of food containing sugar?

Module test questions

1 The table is about cells and the jobs the different parts have.
Match words from the list with each of the numbers **1–4** in the table.

nucleus
cytoplasm
cell wall
chloroplast

	Job
1	traps the Sun's energy for photosynthesis
2	controls the activities of a cell
3	maintains the cell's rigid shape
4	where the cell reactions take place

2 These sentences are about transport systems in a plant.
Choose words from the list for each of the spaces **1–4** in the sentences.

xylem
stomata
guard cells
phloem

Carbon dioxide is able to enter a plant through holes in the leaves called ____**1**____ . The size of these holes is controlled by the ____**2**____ . Water taken in by the roots is transported by the ____**3**____ to the rest of the plant. At the same time ____**4**____ is carrying sugars from the leaves to other parts of the plant.

3 This questions is about how humans respond.
Match words from the list with each of the numbers **1–4** in the table.

tongue   ear   skin   nose

	Job
1	has receptors sensitive to smell
2	has receptors sensitive to sound
3	has receptors sensitive to taste
4	has receptors sensitive to pressure and temperature

4 The diagrams are of a plant cell and an animal cell.

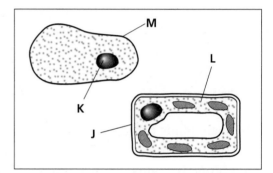

Match words from the list with each of numbers **1–4** in the table.

cell membrane
cell wall
cytoplasm
nucleus

	Part of cell
1	structure J
2	structure K
3	structure L
4	structure M

5 Which *two* of these substances are the products of photosynthesis?

A starch
B glucose
C water
D oxygen
E carbon dioxide.

6 Which *two* of these substances control blood sugar?

A urea
B glucagon
C starch
D glucose
E insulin.

7 This is a diagram of the eye.

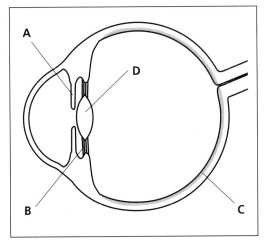

1. Which part is muscular and controls the amount of light entering the eye?

A   B   C   D

2. Which part contains light sensitive cells?

A   B   C   D

3. Which part of the eye focuses light?

A   B   C   D

4. Which part holds the lens in place?

A   B   C   D

8 This question is about plant hormones.

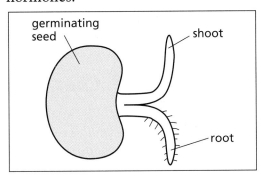

1. Shoots bend upwards as they grow because:

A growth hormone collects on the lower side – this increases the speed of growth, so the lower side grows more slowly
B growth hormone collects on the lower side – this increases the speed of growth, so the lower side grows more quickly
C growth hormone collects on the upper side – this increases the speed of growth, so the upper side grows more quickly
D growth hormone collects on the upper side – this increases the speed of growth, so the upper side grows more slowly.

2. Roots grow downwards because:

A the same amount of hormone increases growth rate in roots
B hormone collects on both upper and lower sides equally
C the hormone collects on the lower side slowing growth
D the hormone collects on the upper side increasing growth.

3. Which of the following is *not* a use of plant growth hormones?

A helping to produce flowers all of the same colour
B helping cuttings to root
C help to ripen fruit when the grower wants
D as weedkillers.

4. To which force do plant roots respond?

A light
B water
C nutrients
D gravity.

Choosing a home

Why do organisms live where they do? You don't see polar bears in Egypt or camels in Canada. One reason is that every organism depends on certain physical factors for it to survive. These factors are:

- temperature – polar bears, for example, like it cold!
- light – plants only grow properly in light conditions
- water – all organisms die without it
- carbon dioxide – for photosynthesis in plants
- oxygen – for respiration in plants and animals.

If the conditions are suitable, then an organism may live, grow and reproduce. If not, the organism isn't found there. Organisms are adapted to live in certain areas. For example, polar bears have very thick fur so they can live in very cold areas. Camels can store water and so can live in hot, dry areas.

✔ **Checkpoint**

Cover the page, then write down the physical factors which affect whether organisms survive or not. Check your answers.

Competition

Plants often compete with each other for space, water and nutrients. For example, a new seedling trying to grow underneath an oak tree is likely to die. The tree's leaves shade it from a lot of the sunlight, and the tree's roots take most of the water and nutrients from the soil. Plants need space to get the water, nutrients and light they need.

Animals often compete with each other for space, food and water. For example, birds have their territories which they protect. They are actually protecting their supply of food and water and, at breeding times, their mates and offspring.

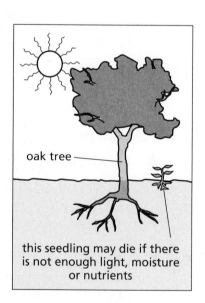

oak tree

this seedling may die if there is not enough light, moisture or nutrients

Predator and prey

Animals which kill and eat other animals are known as **predators**. The animals they kill and eat are known as their **prey**. For example, weasels are predators and mice are some of their prey.

✔ **Checkpoint**

Cover the page, then write down what is meant by the terms **predator** and **prey**. Check your answer.

How big can a population get?

The size of a population of organisms depends on the following things (factors):

- how much food or nutrients is available
- how much competition there is for the food or nutrients
- competition for light (especially for plants)
- how many of the animals are eaten, or how many plants are eaten (grazed) by animals
- how much disease there is.

However, other things affect the size of populations in a group (community) of organisms:

- if the number of predators increases, then the number of prey will decrease (because they are eaten!)
- if the number of prey decreases, then the number of predators will decrease (as there isn't enough to eat!)

This usually means that populations of different organisms (e.g. in a hedgerow) are kept in balance. They remain stable.

 **Help**

Population – the total number of that type of organism in an area. For example, the number of badgers in a wood.
Community – all of the organisms living in a particular area. For example, all of the organisms, including plants, living in a pond.

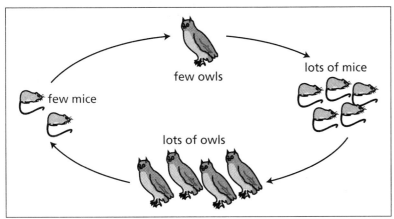

A population cycle

 **Just think!**

There used to be no rabbits in Australia. Someone took some rabbits there. There are now so many that scientists are having to introduce disease to kill them off!

 Questions

1   There is a population of owls in your area. The owls eat small animals and birds. Which of these factors are likely to result in an increase in the owl population?

more light	fewer small animals
more disease	more plant growth
more small birds	less water

2   If the owl population rises, what is likely to happen to the number of small animals?

Food chains, pyramids and webs

What is a food chain?

A **food chain** shows what is eating what. For example:

grass   rabbit   fox

A food chain

Grass is the **producer** in this food chain. It is producing food by photosynthesis. Food chains always start with green plants producing food for all other organisms.

Heat and light (radiation) from the Sun provides the energy for photosynthesis. Green plants can capture only a small part of the Sun's energy. They store it in substances that make up plant cells.

Animals either eat the plants or each other! They are known as **consumers**.

Pyramids of number and biomass

Food webs and chains show us how energy and material is transferred from one organism to another. The numbers of organisms involved at each stage can be shown as a **pyramid of numbers**.

The pyramid on the left shows the numbers of organisms supported in one community. Sometimes, however, a pyramid of numbers (such as the one on the right) does not give a true picture of a food chain.

 **Just think!**

If it wasn't for plants, there would be no life on Earth.

 **Checkpoint**

Cover the page. Can you remember what producers and consumers are? Check your answer.

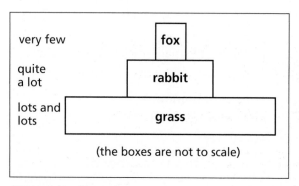

very few	fox
quite a lot	rabbit
lots and lots	grass

(the boxes are not to scale)

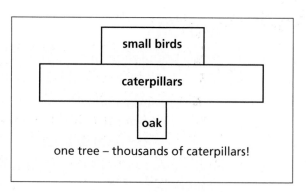

small birds

caterpillars

oak

one tree – thousands of caterpillars!

Pyramids of numbers

A pyramid of numbers can be a strange shape if one of the organisms is large. A **pyramid of biomass** nearly always gives a good idea of the energy and material being transferred up a food chain. Biomass is the mass of living material in a community.

In the pyramid of numbers shown on the opposite page, the tree is a single organism upon which many caterpillars can feed. But this pyramid of biomass gives you a better idea of how much energy the tree supplies.

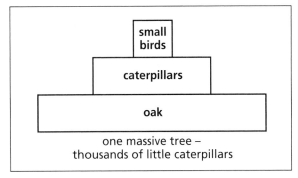

A pyramid of biomass

What are food webs?

In the countryside it is very rare to have a simple food chain. For example, many animals eat grass and lots of animals eat rabbits (e.g. birds of prey such as buzzards and eagles, as well as stoats, weasels and foxes). It's not much of a life being a rabbit!

If we connect up all of the food chains we can make a **food web**. These can be very complicated!

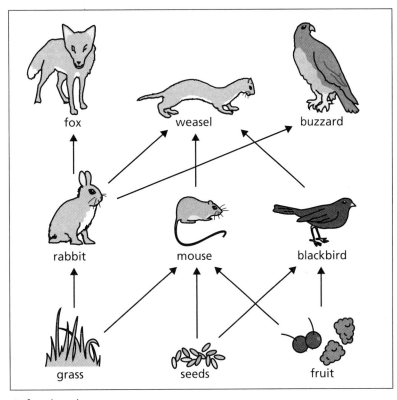

A food web

 Questions

1 In the garden you see blackbirds eating slugs. The slugs feed on green plants. Draw a simple food chain to show this.

2 In the food web shown above:

   a what would happen to the number of blackbirds if there were fewer seeds one year?

   b what would happen to the number of mice if the number of rabbits decreased?

Eating waste

Organisms produce waste:

- some animals produces faeces and urine, which they need to get rid of straight away
- the bodies of all organisms need to decompose after they die.

Microbes break down faeces and dead bodies. These microbes could be bacteria or fungi. The process is known as **decay**.

Microbes work faster if it is warm and wet with plenty of oxygen. They use waste as food to release energy for themselves.

 **Just think!**

If it wasn't for microbes, the planet would be getting deeper and deeper in animal and plant waste!

How do we use microbes?

We use microbes in two ways:

- to break down plants in compost heaps
- to break down sewage on sewage farms.

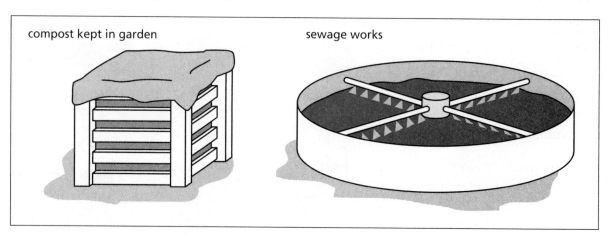

compost kept in garden   sewage works

The process of decay releases substances which plants use to grow. We use the products of compost heaps to fertilise (add nutrients to) our gardens.

The products of the breakdown of sewage can also be used as fertiliser.

If this **recycling** of materials did not take place then, very soon, all of the Earth's materials would be used up.

If a community of organisms takes in and uses as many materials as it releases through decay, the community is said to be **stable**.

The carbon cycle

One important material which is recycled is carbon. This diagram shows how it is used and then recycled to the air ready to be used again.

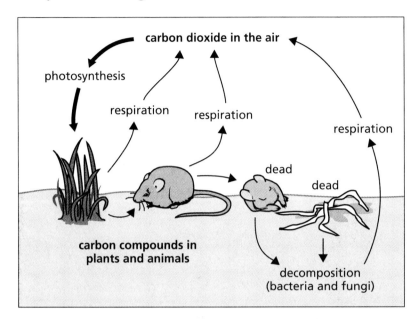

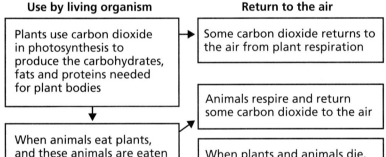

Use by living organism	Return to the air
Plants use carbon dioxide in photosynthesis to produce the carbohydrates, fats and proteins needed for plant bodies	Some carbon dioxide returns to the air from plant respiration
When animals eat plants, and these animals are eaten by other animals, the carbon becomes part of the carbohydrates, fats and proteins in animal bodies	Animals respire and return some carbon dioxide to the air
	When plants and animals die, their bodies are eaten by other animals or microbes, which respire and release carbon dioxide into the air

 **Just think!**

If it wasn't for plants, carbon dioxide in the atmosphere would build up to disastrous levels.

 ## Questions

1 This question is about the carbon cycle. Copy and complete the sentences using these words:

   carbon dioxide   fungi   oxygen   decay   respiration   bacteria

   When a plant dies _____ and _____ break the plant down. They use up _____ and release _____ as the process of _____ is brought about by _____ .

2 Give *two* ways in which humans use microbes.

What about the future?

Up to 200 years ago the human population on Earth was much smaller than it is today and the effect of human activities was small and localised. But the population has grown rapidly over those 200 years and is changing the environment in a number of ways.

Using up the land

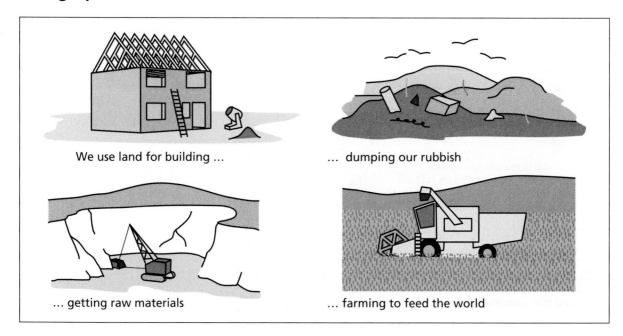

We use land for building ...

... dumping our rubbish

... getting raw materials

... farming to feed the world

Pollution

Water

We pollute water with sewage, fertilisers and poisonous chemicals.

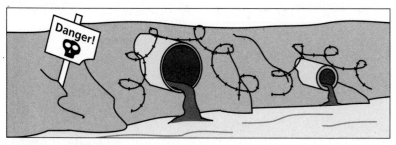

A sewage outfall

Air

We pollute the air when we burn fossil fuels (e.g. coal, oil and gas) releasing carbon dioxide. Burning these fuels also often releases sulphur dioxide and nitrogen oxides into the air.

sulphur dioxide
carbon dioxide

 **Checkpoint**

Cover the page, then write down how acid rain is formed.
Check your answer.

These gases can dissolve in rain to make it acidic. This is called **acid rain**. Acid rain can damage trees. If it makes rivers and lakes too acidic it can kill other plants and animals.

Land

We pollute the land with poisonous chemicals such as pesticides and herbicides (weedkillers). These can be washed into lakes, ponds and rivers.

Are things getting worse?

Yes, they are! There are many more humans now than there used to be. There is more industry. This means:

 **Help**

- the Earth's raw materials (including non-renewable fossil fuels) are being used up more quickly

- we produce more waste – unless we deal with it properly it will cause more and more pollution.

Non-renewable raw materials include coal.
Renewable raw materials include wood.

 Questions

1 Write down *three* ways in which the land available for wildlife has been reduced over the last 200 years.

2 What are the *three* gases which can be given off when fossil fuels are burned?

3 You are travelling in the family car. How is the car helping to produce more acid rain?

Terminal exam questions

1   This is a food web for a wood.

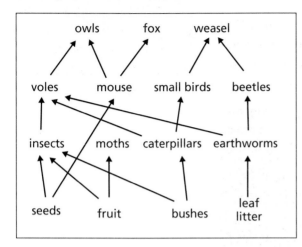

a i Name *two* physical factors which would affect the amount of fruit produced in a year.   [2]

ii Name *two* factors (different from those above) which would affect the population of caterpillars in the wood.   [2]

b i In one year the caterpillar population is very low. What is likely to happen to the population of small birds? Explain your answer.   [2]

ii If the mouse population is low, what effect is this likely to have on the vole population? Explain your answer.   [2]

[8 marks]

2 a i In what form do plants take up carbon from the atmosphere?   [1]

ii Give *two* different uses of carbon in a plant.   [2]

b   Suggest and explain *two* different ways that carbon in a plant may be recycled to the atmosphere.   [4]

c   Name *two* ways in which humans use microbes.   [2]

[9 marks]

3 a i Suggest *two* reasons for pollution being an increasing problem on the planet.   [2]

ii Suggest *two* reasons for the amount of land available to plants and animals becoming less and less.   [2]

b   State *three* ways in which humans are polluting the planet.   [3]

[7 marks]

4   This is a pyramid of numbers for a food chain in a pond.

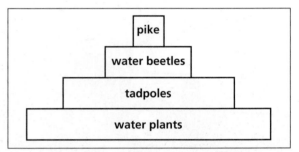

a i Which organism is the producer?   [1]

ii Which organism is the top predator? [1]

iii Name *one* organism which acts as prey.   [1]

b   Name *two* different things the tadpoles might compete for.   [2]

c   This is a pyramid of numbers for a food chain that might be found in a garden.

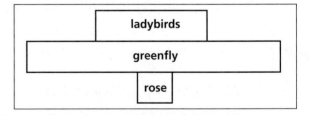

Why might a pyramid of biomass give you a better picture of what is going on?   [1]

[6 marks]

Total for test: 30 marks

Why do we look like we do?

Similarities

People often look a bit like one or both of their parents. This is because male and female sex cells from their parents have joined together to form them. The sex cells pass on some of the **characteristics** of the parents' to their children.

Family members can look similar ...

When an animal or plant is growing the body cells divide to provide more cells for growth. We also need to replace cells which are destroyed or worn away.

Differences

But, although children might look like their parents in some ways, overall they are different. This is because the 'mix' of characteristics which they have is different to both of their parents'. Some may be boys and some girls. But other characteristics might be different as well (e.g. eye colour, height). This is because each sex cell contains a different combination of the parents' characteristics.

... and different too!

Other reasons for differences

The other reasons for differences between individual plants or animals are **environmental**. This means the conditions in which an individual has grown up. Examples in animals are how much food they have or whether they catch disease, and so on. For plants it might be the amount of light, water and nutrients they have.

Reproduction and variation

Genes and chromosomes

Characteristics are controlled by **genes**. The nucleus of every cell in your body contains genes which carry the plans for your body's development. Different genes control different characteristics (e.g. eye colour, nose shape).

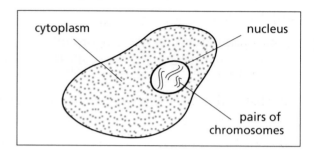

The nucleus of every cell contains **chromosomes** which are made up of many genes. The chromosomes in the body cells are in pairs.

The number of chromosome pairs in body cells is different for each type of plant or animal. Human body cells have 23 pairs, making 46 chromosomes altogether.

One of these pairs of chromosomes carries the genes which decide the sex of a person. In girls and women the chromosomes in the pair are the same (**XX**). In boys and men they are different (**XY**).

Help

Chromosomes are made up of **genes**. Genes that control the same characteristic are called **alleles**. Alleles are found in pairs.

Each chromosome in a pair is made up of genes which control the same characteristics (e.g. a person's sex). So the genes themselves are also in pairs. These pairs of genes are called **alleles**.

Sometimes the two genes in these pairs carry different information for the characteristics they both control. For example in the pair of genes controlling someone's eye colour, there may be one allele for blue and one allele for brown.

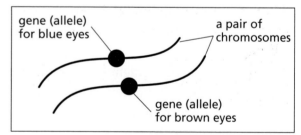

Inheriting disorders

Children can inherit disorders from their parents as well as eye colour and height. Two disorders which can be inherited are:

- Huntington's chorea – this affects the nervous system. If one parent has the disorder, the child may inherit it.

- Cystic fibrosis – this is a disorder of cell membranes. Both parents have to carry the gene for a child to inherit the disorder. If only one parent is a carrier, or if one parent has the disorder and the other is not a carrier, then none of the children will have it.

Help

A **carrier** is someone whose cells carry a gene for a particular disorder, but the person does not show signs of the disorder itself.

Sexual reproduction

In the sex cells, just as other body cells:

- the nucleus controls the cell
- chromosomes are in the nucleus
- each gene controls a characteristic.

In body cells, chromosomes are found in pairs. On these chromosomes pairs of genes (alleles) control the same characteristic (e.g. eye colour). In sex cells, however, there is only one allele from each pair. This is because there is only one chromosome from each pair.

In **sexual reproduction** a male sex cell and a female sex cell join together. Sex cells are also called **gametes** (in humans these are the sperm and egg). The offspring are all different. Another way of putting this is to say that they vary, and so these differences are known as **variation**.

Help

A human body cell has 46 chromosomes (23 pairs). A human sex cell has 23 chromosomes.

Asexual reproduction

There are no sex cells involved at all in **asexual reproduction**. It is really reproduction by growth. For example, if you plant one daffodil bulb then several years later there will be a number of bulbs. The new bulbs grow from the original one. There are now more bulbs than when you started, so reproduction has taken place.

The new bulbs are exact copies of the parent, with exactly the same genes. We call them **clones**.

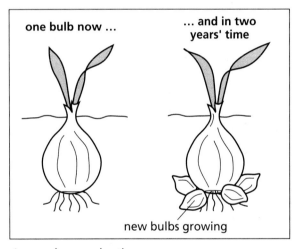

Asexual reproduction

Questions

1 Copy and complete the sentences, using words from this list:

   chromosomes   alleles   nucleus   genes

   The genetic material in human cells is found in the _____ . In each human body cell there are 23 pairs of _____ which are made up of _____ . These are also found in pairs and sometimes carry different information for the same characteristic. These are known as _____ .

2 Why is a clone the same as its parent?

Controlling reproduction

Breeding the animals and plants we want

We may grow a particularly pretty red rose. How do we get another one? It's simple – we take a cutting and it will grow into a plant exactly like the parent.

A cutting needs warm, wet conditions for the new roots to grow well.

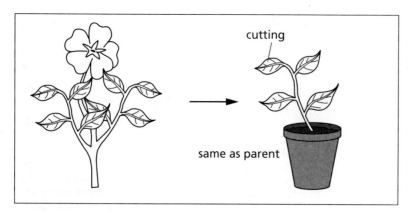

What if we want a fast horse?

You can't just cut a piece off and grow it! You have to breed together a fast male horse and fast female horse. Hopefully the foal will also be fast. This is known as **selective breeding**.

We do this with many animals and plants. For example, we selectively breed:

- cows to produce more milk
- pigs to produce leaner bacon
- wheat to produce more seed
- peaches to produce sweeter fruit.

 **Checkpoint**

Cover the page, then write down what is meant by 'selective breeding'. Check your answer.

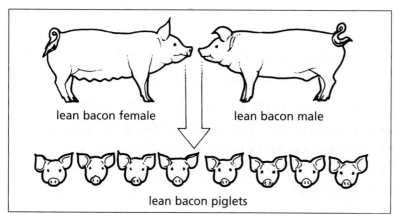

Selective breeding of pigs

Controlling human reproduction

We often want to control our own reproduction, but not for selective breeding purposes! We do it to avoid having babies, or to increase the chances of having them.

One way of doing both is for women to control their **fertility**. Fertility means the ability to reproduce. A woman's fertility is controlled by hormones in her body which:

- release an egg from her ovaries every month
- make the lining of her womb thicker to receive the egg if it is fertilised.

Help

Hormones are chemical messengers in the body.

These hormones are produced (secreted) by the pituitary gland in her brain and by the ovaries themselves.

Hormones which are produced artificially can be used to stop the woman's ovaries producing eggs. This is how the birth control pill works. It is the most reliable method of contraception but, for a few women, can produce unpleasant side-effects. These include giddiness, nausea or, very occasionally, thrombosis (blood clots).

If a woman's ovaries are not releasing an egg every month she may find it difficult to conceive a child when she does want one. Other artificially produced hormones can stimulate the release of eggs from her ovaries. These are fertility drugs.

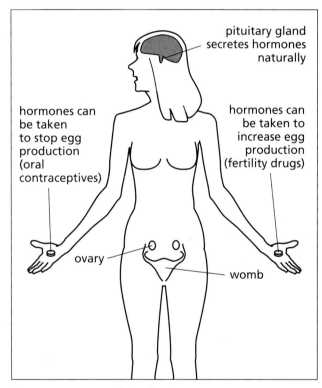

Hormones control fertility in women

Questions

1   What conditions are necessary for a cutting to grow new roots properly?

2   Copy and complete the sentences using these words:

       fertility   hormones   pituitary gland   secreted

The ability of a woman to have a child is controlled by chemical messengers called _____ . This ability is known as the woman's _____ . The chemical messengers are produced by the _____ . Another word for produced is _____ .

Extinction and evolution

How do species develop?

We know that some species which existed thousands or millions of years ago have died out because we have found their remains in rocks as **fossils**.

Fossils are formed:

- from the hard parts of plants and animals (bits that do not decay easily)
- from other parts which did not decay because there was no oxygen (for the bacteria to use)
- when parts of the animal or plant were replaced by other materials as they decayed.

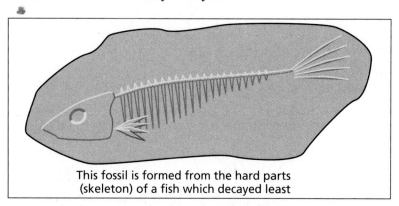

This fossil is formed from the hard parts (skeleton) of a fish which decayed least

Fossils give us a picture of how species have changed (**evolved**) over millions of years. We know that all living things on the planet today have come from organisms that first developed over three billion years ago. These were very simple life forms. This is called the **theory of evolution**.

The diagram shows how the horse has evolved.

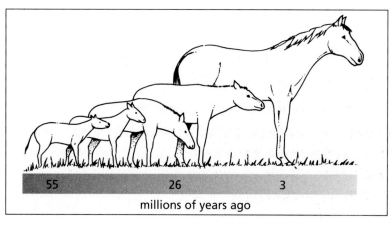

55   26   3

millions of years ago

Evolution of the horse

Help

A **species** is a group of one sort of organism. For example, lions are a species.

Checkpoint

Cover the page, then write down how fossils may be formed.
Check your answer.

How do species die?

Species die out (become **extinct**) for a number of reasons:

- their environment changes (e.g. it gets warmer or colder on the planet)
- predators eat them all, or disease kills them all
- another species competes successfully against them (e.g. for food).

How do new species begin?

Sometimes when conditions change a new species develops from an existing one.

A change in members of the species might be caused by a **mutation**. This is a change in the genes of an organism.

Mutations occur naturally. However, there is more chance of a mutation if an organism is exposed to:

- ionising radiation (e.g. ultraviolet light, X-rays)
- radioactive substances
- some chemicals.

The more you are exposed to these things, the greater the chance of a mutation.

 **Just think!**

If someone is pregnant a doctor may say no to an X-ray, in case it causes a mutation in the baby.

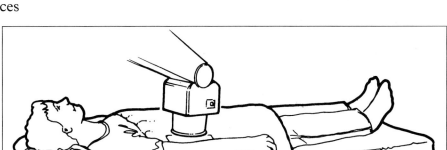

Too many X-rays may cause a mutation

 Questions

1. What is a mutation?
2. State *three* things which might cause a species to die out.
3. Copy and complete the following sentences using words from this list:

    evolution   extinction   mutation

    A _____ is a change in a species which may result in _____. If the change results in a species dying out this is known as _____.

Terminal exam questions

1 a Copy and complete the following sentences. Use words from this list to fill spaces **1–4**:

alleles
chromosomes
genes
nucleus

The ____1____ controls the cell. Within this part of the human cell are pairs of ____2____. These are made up of ____3____ which control characteristics such as eye colour. They may be found in two different forms called ____4____, for example blue and brown eye colour.   [4]

b i Why do gardeners take cuttings?   [1]

ii Sometimes the new plants are not identical to the parent.
Suggest *one* reason for this.   [1]

iii Name *two* conditions necessary for cuttings to grow well.   [2]

[8 marks]

2 a i Which part of a cell does cystic fibrosis affect?   [1]

ii How is the disease inherited?   [2]

b i Name *one* symptom of Huntington's chorea.   [1]

ii How is this disease inherited?   [2]

[6 marks]

3 a Suggest *three* reasons for a species dying out.   [3]

b Explain fully why mutations can be harmful.   [4]

[7 marks]

4 a i What is meant by the term 'selective breeding'?   [2]

ii Why is selective breeding carried out?   [2]

b How do hormones help in:

i birth control?   [2]

ii fertility treatment?   [2]

[8 marks]

5 This strawberry plant is producing new strawberry plants.

a What type of reproduction is taking place?   [1]

b Why will all of the new strawberry plants be the same as the parent strawberry plant?   [2]

c How would you go about breeding a new strawberry plant which develops bigger strawberries?   [2]

[5 marks]

Total for test: 34 marks

AT3

Materials and their Properties

Metals

Earth Materials

Patterns of Chemical Change

Structures and Bonding

Metals and their uses

What are metals?

We all know what iron and gold look like. They are metals. However, most people would not think of sodium and potassium as metals. They look different.

Metals have these properties:

- all are solid at room temperature (except mercury)
- they have high melting points
- they are shiny (when freshly cut)
- they form alloys (mixtures of metals)
- most are strong and tough – they can be hammered or bent into shape
- they are good conductors of heat and electricity (whether solids or liquids).

Over 75% of all elements are metals.

Checkpoint

Cover the page, then write down *three* properties of metals.
Check your answer.

What are metals used for?

You need to know about three metals – copper, iron and aluminium.

Metal	Properties	Uses
copper	conducts electricity well can be shaped easily	in electrical circuits as copper wire for water pipes and tanks
iron	is strong and tough	in car and bridge construction
aluminium	is strong with a low density	for aircraft manufacture

What about non-metals?

Less than 25% of the elements are non-metals (e.g. oxygen, chlorine, sulphur).

Most non-metals have these properties:

- low melting and boiling points – most are gases at room temperature
- they are dull in appearance
- they are brittle and dull when solid
- they are poor conductors of heat and electricity – whether solid or liquid.

Checkpoint

Cover the page, then write down *three* properties of non-metals.
Check your answer.

Which metals are most reactive?

We can tell this by looking at how quickly metals react with air, water and dilute acids.

- **With air**
  Metals react with air to produce metal oxides. For example:

  magnesium + oxygen → magnesium oxide

- **With water**
  Metals react with water (cold, hot or as steam) to produce metal hydroxides or oxides plus hydrogen. For example:

  calcium + water → calcium hydroxide + hydrogen

- **With dilute acids**
  Metals react with dilute acids to produce metal salts and hydrogen. For example:

  $$\textbf{zinc} + \textbf{hydrochloric acid} \rightarrow \textbf{zinc chloride} + \textbf{hydrogen}$$

A more reactive metal will displace a less reactive metal from its compounds. For example:

$$\textbf{aluminium} + \textbf{iron(III) oxide} \rightarrow \textbf{iron} + \textbf{aluminium oxide}$$

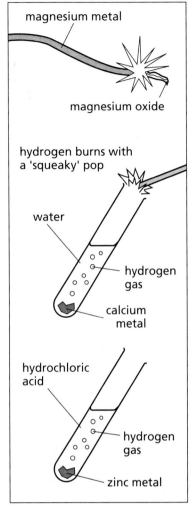

The reactions of metals

Questions

1 Copy and complete the three equations using these words:

   oxygen   hydrogen   hydroxide   hydrochloric

   magnesium + _____ → magnesium oxide

   calcium + water → calcium _____ + hydrogen

   zinc + _____ acid → zinc chloride + _____

2 Draw up a table with two columns. At the top of the columns write the headings **Metals** and **Non–metals**.

   Put the following properties of substances into your table, placing each property in one column only:

brittle when solid	**most are gases at room temperature**
shiny when cut	**good conductors of electricity**
form alloys	**poor conductors of heat.**

Metal ores

Most metals are found in the Earth's crust in compounds with other elements (e.g. metal oxides). They are often mixed up with other compounds in the rocks as well. Before we can use these metals they have to be separated from other elements. This may be done chemically.

Any rock which contains enough of a metal or its compounds to make it worth extracting is called an **ore**.

Extracting metal

If a metal is found as a metal oxide the oxygen has to be removed to leave the metal behind. This removal of oxygen is called **reduction**. It can be done by using a more reactive substance to 'bully' the metal out of its compound.

Carbon is more reactive than iron so we can use it to take the oxygen from the iron in the iron oxide found in the ore.

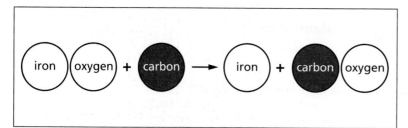

Carbon removes the oxygen from the iron

You need to heat the substances before the reaction will work. This is done in a **blast furnace**. The reaction is shown on the opposite page.

The blast furnace

Also in the blast furnace:

- there are acid impurities in the iron ore – these sink to the bottom
- limestone is added to the reaction chamber
- the limestone reacts with the acid impurities to produce 'slag'
- this is 'run off' from the bottom of the blast furnace and got rid of.

Help

Some metals in order of their reactivity:

potassium (K)	**most**
sodium (Na)	**reactive**
calcium (Ca)	
magnesium (Mg)	
aluminium (Al)	
carbon (C)	
zinc (Zn)	
iron (Fe)	
tin (Sb)	
lead (Pb)	
copper (Cu)	
silver (Ag)	**least**
gold (Au)	**reactive**

You do not need to remember this table.

This is what happens in the reaction chamber:

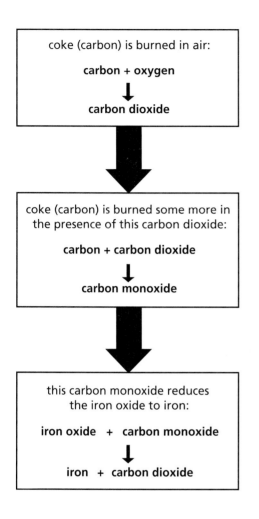

coke (carbon) is burned in air:

carbon + oxygen
↓
carbon dioxide

coke (carbon) is burned some more in the presence of this carbon dioxide:

carbon + carbon dioxide
↓
carbon monoxide

this carbon monoxide reduces the iron oxide to iron:

iron oxide + carbon monoxide
↓
iron + carbon dioxide

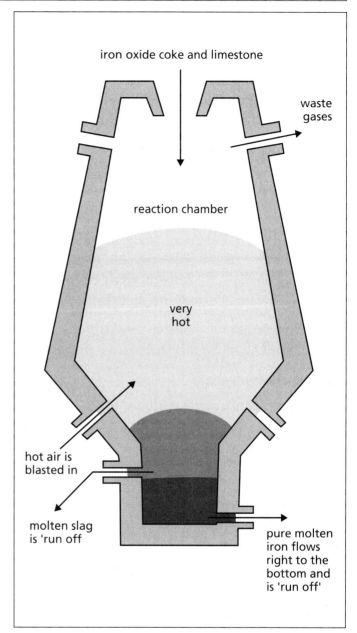

iron oxide coke and limestone

waste gases

reaction chamber

very hot

hot air is blasted in

molten slag is 'run off'

pure molten iron flows right to the bottom and is 'run off'

The blast furnace

Questions

1 Copy and complete the sentences, using words from this list:

> **less   reduce   iron   more**
> **slag   carbon monoxide   calcium carbonate**

Carbon can _____ iron oxide to _____ as carbon is _____ reactive than iron. In fact, it is actually _____ that reacts with iron. Limestone (_____) is added to react with any impurities and form _____ .

Extracting aluminium

The most difficult metals to extract are the most reactive ones, because it is difficult for other elements to push them out of their compounds. The least reactive metals (e.g. gold) are found just as the metals, not in compounds.

Aluminium is much more reactive than iron. It is also more reactive than carbon, so carbon cannot be used to reduce aluminium.

Aluminium is extracted from its ore (aluminium oxide) by **electrolysis**. Aluminium oxide is made up of positive aluminium ions and negative oxygen ions. When substances are made of **ions** they can be broken down by passing an electric current through them.

The substance has to be molten (melted) or dissolved before this will work. Why? So that the ions are free to move.

During electrolysis:

• the positive aluminium ions move to the negative electrode

• the negative oxygen ions move to the positive electrode.

Electrolysis is used to extract most reactive metals from their ores. The pure metals are always formed at the negative electrode and a gas is often given off at the positive electrode.

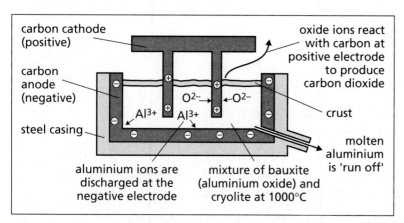

The extraction of aluminium

How does the process work?

Aluminium oxide has a very high melting point, but it can be dissolved in molten cryolite at a much lower temperature. This saves the manufacturers lots of money because they use less energy to heat the ore.

Just think!

Gold is found as pure metal. All of the gold ever found would fit under the bottom of the Eiffel Tower!

Just think!

The aluminium foil in your kitchen was once a rock!

The electrodes are made of carbon. Aluminium forms at the negative electrode. Oxygen forms at the positive electrode – this makes the electrode burn away quickly so it has to be replaced often.

Purifying copper

Very pure copper is needed for electricity wires. We get it by purifying impure copper using electrolysis.

A positive electrode made of impure copper is dipped in a solution of copper sulphate. Positive copper ions move to the negative electrode and pure copper collects there.

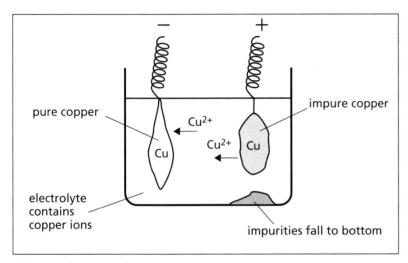

The purification of copper

Questions

1   This question is about the electrolysis of aluminium. Copy and complete the sentences using these words:

negative   oxide   positive   cryolite

The ore of aluminium is aluminium _____ . It has a high melting point so is added to molten _____ . The aluminium ions are deposited at the _____ electrode and the oxygen ions move to the _____ electrode.

2   Why do substances have to be dissolved or melted if they are going to be electrolysed?

3   Using information from both this spread and the previous spread place these three elements in a reactivity series:

aluminium (Al)   carbon (C)   iron (Fe)

From other knowledge you have of chemistry now add sodium (Na) and gold (Au) to your reactivity series.

Properties of compounds

Some metal and non-metal compounds dissolve in water.

Non-metals

Soluble oxides of non-metals (e.g. carbon dioxide, sulphur dioxide and nitrogen dioxide) produce acidic solutions. For example:

carbon dioxide + water → carbonic acid

It is these gases which dissolve in rain water to cause acid rain.

Metals

Some metal oxides and hydroxides (e.g. the oxides and hydroxides of sodium, potassium and, to some extent, calcium) dissolve in water to produce alkaline solutions. For example:

potassium + water → hydrogen + potassium hydroxide

Potassium hydroxide dissolves in water to produce an alkaline solution.

Measuring pH

A solution may be neutral, acidic or alkaline. Water is neutral. Indicators show the pH of a liquid.

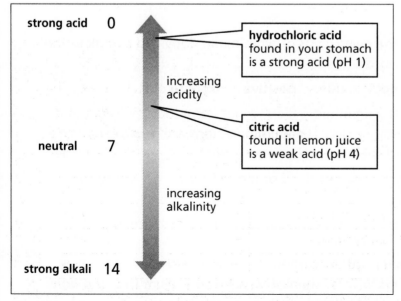

The pH scale

 **Checkpoint**

Cover the page, then write down the pH of a strong alkali.
Check your answer.

Neutralisation

An acid and an alkali react together to produce a salt plus water – this is a **neutralisation** reaction.

> **acid + alkali →**
> **salt + water**

The salt produced depends on:

- the metal in the alkali
- the acid used.

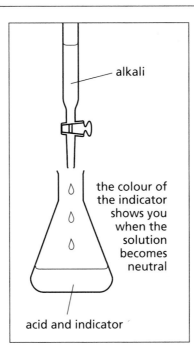

alkali

the colour of the indicator shows you when the solution becomes neutral

acid and indicator

 **Help**

Sodium chloride is a salt. It is also called 'salt'.
There are many other salts (e.g. potassium nitrate, calcium sulphate).
So salt is not the only salt!

Neutralising hydrochloric acid produces chlorides:

> **hydrochloric acid + sodium hydroxide → sodium chloride + water**

Neutralising nitric acid produces nitrates:

> **nitric acid + sodium hydroxide → sodium nitrate + water**

Neutralising sulphuric acid produces sulphates:

> **sulphuric acid + sodium hydroxide → sodium sulphate + water**

 Just think!

If you have a stomach upset it could be due to too much acid. You could buy 'Milk of Magnesia' (an alkali) to neutralise your stomach acid and cure the upset.

 ## Questions

1 This question is about neutralisation reactions. Copy and complete the table, using these words:

potassium nitrate   sodium nitrate   potassium sulphate   calcium chloride

Acid	Alkali	Products	
sulphuric acid	+ potassium hydroxide	→	+ water
nitric acid	+ potassium hydroxide	→	+ water
hydrochloric acid	+ calcium hydroxide	→	+ water
nitric acid	+ sodium hydroxide	→	+ water

2 Name *two* gases (other than carbon dioxide) which cause acid rain.

Module test questions

1   This question is about the pH scale. Match words from the list with the labels **1–4** on the diagram.

weak alkali
weak acid
neutral
strong acid

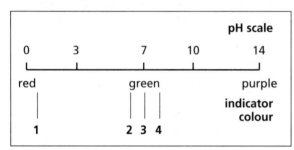

2   This question is about the different types of chemical reaction.
Match words from the list with each of numbers **1–4** in the table.

displacement
reduction
neutralisation
oxidation

	Description
1	the reaction between an acid and an alkali
2	when a metal oxide loses its oxygen
3	when a metal becomes a metal oxide
4	when a more reactive metal removes a less reactive metal from a compound

3   This table is about the reactions of some metals.
Choose words from the list for each of the numbers **1–4** in the table.

metal oxide
metal chloride
hydrogen
metal hydroxide or oxide

	Reaction
1	the result of the reaction between a metal and hydrochloric acid
2	the result of the reaction between a metal and oxygen
3	the gas given off when a metal reacts with hydrochloric acid
4	the result of a reaction between metal and water

4   These sentences are about the use of some metals.
Use words from the list to fill in the spaces **1–4** in the sentences.

a good conductor of electricity
strong
strong with a low density
easily shaped

Iron is used to build bridges because it is ____1____.
Copper is used in electric wiring because it is ____2____ and to make water pipes because it is ____3____.
Aluminium is used in the manufacture of aeroplanes because it is ____4____.

5   When hydrochloric acid and sodium hydroxide react together the *two* products are:

A sodium chloride
B hydrogen
C carbon dioxide
D sodium sulphate
E water.

6 In the electrolysis of aluminium oxide (bauxite), which *two* of the following statements are correct?

A cryolite is a useful source of aluminium

B aluminium forms at the negative electrode

C the electrodes are made of aluminium

D oxygen forms at the negative electrode

E the electrodes are made of carbon.

7 This is a picture of a blast furnace.

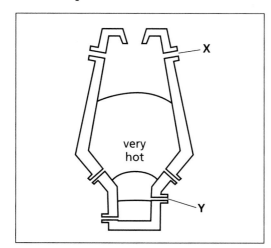

1. What happens at **X**?

A waste gases are given off

B molten iron flows

C molten slag is run off

D hot air is blasted in.

2. What happens at **Y**?

A waste gases are given off

B molten iron flows

C molten slag is run off

D hot air is blasted in.

3. Which substance is formed first when coke burns in the furnace?

A carbon

B carbon dioxide

C slag

D carbon monoxide.

4. The substance which reduces the iron is:

A carbon dioxide

B limestone

C carbon monoxide

D carbon.

8 This question is about the oxides of non-metals.

1. When carbon dioxide dissolves in water, which of the following is formed?

A carbonic acid

B a carbonate

C a carbohydrate

D carbolic acid.

2. For an oxide to dissolve in water it must:

A be insoluble

B form a precipitate

C be soluble

D react and give off a gas.

3. Two gases which are responsible for acid rain are:

A sulphur dioxide and hydrogen chloride

B nitrogen oxides and sulphur dioxide

C chlorine and nitrogen dioxide

D hydrogen sulphide and sulphur dioxide.

4. You can neutralise an acid with:

A an alkali

B hydrogen

C a non-metal oxide

D a salt.

How Earth is formed

The Earth is nearly a sphere (a ball shape). It has a layered structure, which includes:

- a thin crust

- a very viscous mantle (very thick liquid) which goes almost half way to the Earth's centre

- a core in the centre, containing nickel and iron – the outer part is liquid and the inner part solid.

The rocks which make up the Earth's crust are not as dense as the Earth as a whole. This means that the inside of the Earth must be made of different materials, which are more dense than the crust.

The Earth's surface is made of continental crust and oceanic crust. The rocks in continental crust are described as 'granitic'. They are slightly less dense than the oceanic rocks, which are described as 'basaltic'. This means that the continental crust rises above the ocean bed, forming dry land above sea level.

The pattern of continents

The edges of continents are sometimes separated by thousands of kilometres of ocean. It seems that their shapes could fit together quite well (e.g. South America and Africa). They also seem to have similar patterns of rocks and fossils. This suggests that they were once joined together and over millions of years have moved apart.

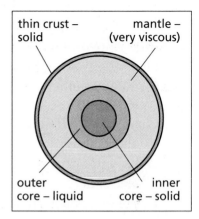

The structure of the Earth

Checkpoint

Cover the page, then write down what the outer part of the Earth is called.
Check your answer.

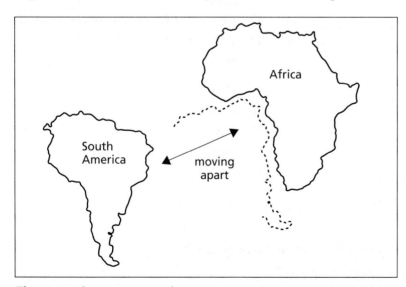

These continents are moving apart

Tectonic plates

The Earth's crust is split into a number of very large pieces – rather like a jigsaw. These pieces are called **tectonic plates**, which 'float' on the mantle underneath. The plates are moving by a few centimetres every year because of convection currents in the mantle. The energy for this comes from heat released by radioactive processes inside the Earth.

Do not try to remember this map!

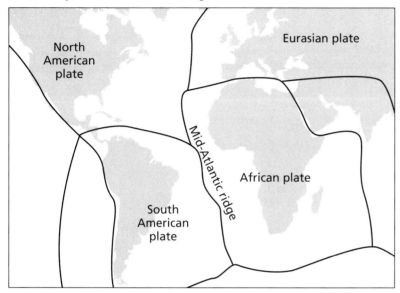

Tectonic plates

We now know that mountains have been formed when plates have collided with each other, forcing one of the plates upwards.

It used to be believed that as the Earth cooled its circumference became smaller, and that this 'shrinking' forced rocks upwards.

 **Checkpoint**

Cover the page, then write down why the tectonic plates are constantly moving. Check your answer.

 Questions

1 Why do we think that the continents are moving apart?

2 What causes the tectonic plates to move?

Rock types and their formation

Sedimentary rocks

These were formed from layers of sediment (such as sand, mud or the shells of dead shellfish) deposited on top of one another. The weight squeezes out the water and sediment becomes cemented together, with other fragments, by salts crystallising out of the water. The process often takes millions of years.

These rocks include:

• **sandstone** – made of grains of sand

• **limestone** – made from calcium carbonate (often from shell remains of living organisms).

Sedimentary rocks, on the surface, usually lie on top of older rocks. These rock layers can be:

• tilted   • folded

• fractured (faults)   • and sometimes turned upside down!

Checkpoint

Cover the page, then write down how sedimentary rocks are formed.
Check your answer.

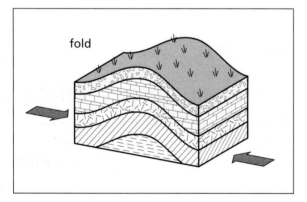
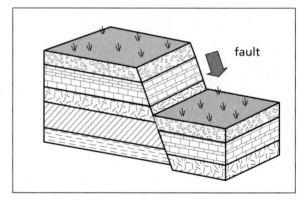

These movements are caused by very large forces. Large-scale Earth movements can, over a long time, cause mountain ranges to form. These replace older mountains which have been worn down (eroded) by the weather.

Igneous rocks

These are formed from molten rock (magma).

If molten rock is forced from inside the Earth up into the crust (but not onto the surface) it then cools and forms **intrusive** igneous rock (e.g. granite).

If the molten rock erupts onto the surface (e.g. from a volcano) it forms **extrusive** igneous rock (e.g. basalt).

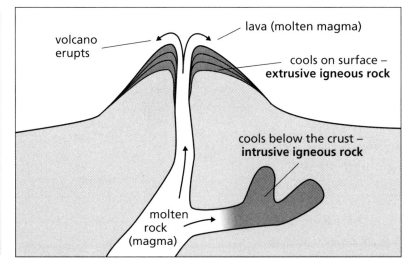

Igneous rock

Rocks made of randomly arranged interlocking crystals (of a number of different minerals) are likely to be igneous.

If the molten rock cools quickly (e.g. from a volcano) the crystals will probably be small. Larger crystals are likely to be in igneous rocks which have cooled below the Earth's surface or in the sea.

Metamorphic rocks

These are often found in present day and old mountain ranges. They are formed when there is high temperature and pressure, often caused by the mountain building process.

Metamorphic rocks are igneous or sedimentary rocks which have been buried underground by the Earth's movements. They become compressed and heated. Their texture may change without the rock melting.

These rocks include:

- **marble** – formed in this way from limestone
- **shale** – formed from mudstone
- **schist** – rocks composed of bands of interlocking crystals are likely to be metamorphic. Schist is a good example.

Just think!

Most marble was formed from other rocks when mountains were being made.

Questions

1 How is sedimentary rock formed?

2 A piece of igneous rock is made up from very small crystals. What does this tell you about how it was formed?

3 How can sedimentary and igneous rocks become metamorphic rocks?

Why is limestone so useful?

Limestone, a sedimentary rock, is mainly calcium carbonate. It can be quarried and used as a building material. Powdered limestone can be used to neutralise acidity in lakes and soils.

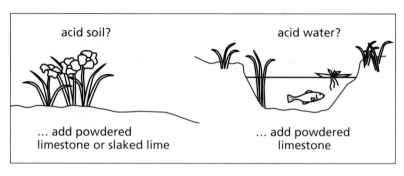

acid soil?

... add powdered limestone or slaked lime

acid water?

... add powdered limestone

If you heat limestone in a kiln then **quicklime** is produced (calcium oxide). This reacts with water to produce **slaked lime** (calcium hydroxide). This reduces soil acidity.

Cement is made by roasting powdered limestone with powdered clay in a rotary kiln. If it is mixed with water, sand and crushed rock then a slow chemical reaction produces a hard, stone-like building material called **concrete**.

Glass is made by heating a mixture of limestone, sand and soda (sodium carbonate).

glass vase made from limestone, sand and soda

Fossils

Sedimentary rocks often contain fossils. As the sediment is laid down, parts of plants and animals may be trapped and preserved in the rock. This means that each layer contains fossils of the same age.

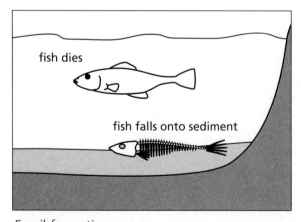

fish dies

fish falls onto sediment

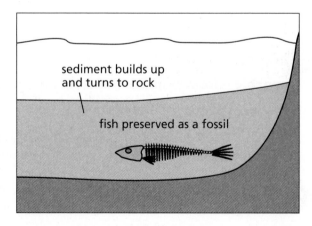

sediment builds up and turns to rock

fish preserved as a fossil

Fossil formation

Fossils can therefore be used to identify rocks of the same age in different areas – but they cannot be used to date rocks accurately. They can be used to find out if rocks are younger or older than each other.

The rock cycle

The crust of the Earth is continually moving. This causes changes which include some mountains being formed and others being worn away. It also results in the rock cycle which takes place continuously but is very slow.

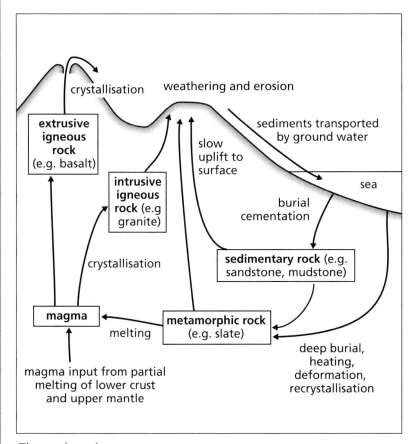

The rock cycle

 ### Questions

1   This question is about limestone. Copy and complete the sentences using these words:

> **calcium carbonate   cement   slaked lime   quicklime**

Limestone is mainly _____ . When it is heated _____ is produced (calcium oxide). This can be reacted with water to produce _____ (calcium hydroxide). If you roast powdered limestone with powdered clay then you have made _____ .

2   How can fossils be used to identify rocks of the same age?

3   Study the diagram of the rock cycle. How could sedimentary rock eventually become igneous rock?

Crude oil and its products

Crude oil is obtained from the Earth's crust. It was formed from the remains of organisms which lived millions of years ago. Crude oil, like coal and natural gas, is a **fossil fuel**.

It was produced as a result of heat and pressure (in the absence of air) acting on the remains of animals and plants trapped in sedimentary rock. This process took millions of years.

Oil and gas are less dense than water. They rise to the top of porous rock, like water through a sponge. They are then trapped below non-porous rock. We get the oil and gas by drilling down through the non-porous layer of rock.

Help

Porous rock allows liquids to pass through it.
Non-porous rock doesn't!

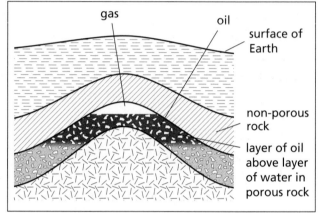

Where oil is found

Separating crude oil

Crude oil is a mixture of very many compounds. A mixture is made up of two or more elements or compounds which are not chemically combined together. This means that mixtures can be separated by physical processes such as dissolving and filtration.

Oil is separated by **distillation** – it is heated and then the gases that come off are cooled so that they turn back into liquids.

Most of the compounds in oil are made up of hydrogen and carbon only, and so are called **hydrocarbons**. These different hydrocarbons can be separated by evaporating the oil, then condensing the gases which evaporate at different temperatures. A different **fraction** comes off at each temperature. Each fraction consists of a type of hydrocarbon which has molecules with a similar number of carbon atoms. This is known as **fractional distillation**.

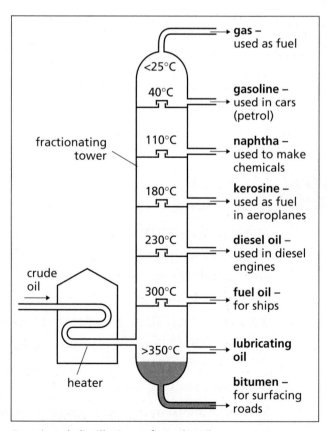

Fractional distillation of crude oil

Hydrocarbon molecules in crude oil vary a great deal in size. The larger the molecule (which means it has more carbon atoms) the:

- higher the boiling point
- less volatile it is (this means it is more difficult to evaporate)
- less easily it flows (this means it is more viscous)
- less easy it is to ignite (this means it is less flammable).

Larger hydrocarbons can be broken down into smaller, more useful hydrocarbons. This is called **cracking**. Some of these hydrocarbons are used as fuels and some are used to make plastics. Some examples are shown in the diagram.

Two different hydrocarbons

'Cracking' a hydrocarbon

Plastics include polythene and PVC.

Questions

1 These are two hydrocarbons:
   a Which is the most flammable?
   b Which has the higher boiling point?
   c Which is the more volatile?

2 Copy and complete the sentences, choosing words from this list:

   less dense   porous   more dense   non-porous

   Oil is found above _____ rock as it is _____ than water. Oil is trapped below _____ rock.

3 Why do we find oil above porous rock?

Does burning fuel pollute?

Yes it does! Gases are produced by the combustion (burning) of fuels. The fuels react with oxygen in the air. These reactions produce oxides.

Most fuels contain carbon and/or hydrogen. Some also contain sulphur. The gases produced when these substances burn include:

- carbon dioxide (from the carbon)
- sulphur dioxide (from the sulphur)
- water vapour (from the burning of hydrogen).

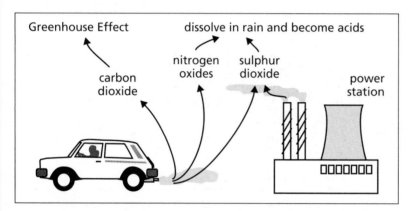

The Greenhouse Effect

The amount of carbon dioxide in the atmosphere is increasing because we burn fossil fuels. Carbon dioxide traps energy (heat) from the Sun in our atmosphere. This makes the atmosphere warm up, causing the polar ice to melt and sea levels to rise.

Carbon dioxide is therefore known as a 'Greenhouse' gas.

 **Just think!**

If the Greenhouse Effect continues then large areas of Britain may be flooded.

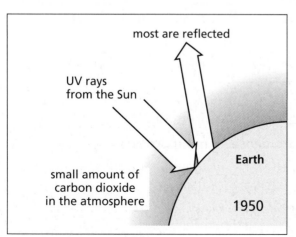

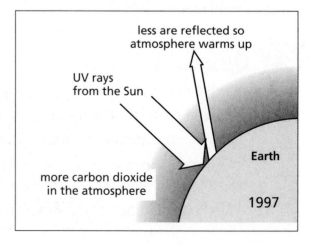

The Greenhouse Effect

What is acid rain?

Burning fuels results in high temperatures. This may cause nitrogen in the air to react with oxygen to form nitrogen oxides.

Sulphur dioxide and nitrogen oxides produced by furnaces and car engines dissolve in rain, making it acidic. This 'acid rain' may fall on lakes, rivers and ponds making the water so acidic that the organisms in it die.

Help

Acid rain can also damage the stonework and metalwork on buildings.

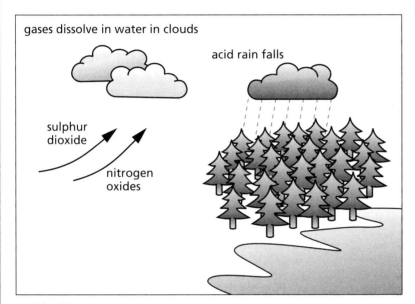

gases dissolve in water in clouds

acid rain falls

sulphur dioxide

nitrogen oxides

Acid rain

For the last 200 million years the atmosphere has been made up from:

- about 80% nitrogen
- about 20% oxygen
- small amounts of other gases (e.g. carbon dioxide, water, and the noble gases neon and argon).

Checkpoint

Cover the page, then write down the *two* gases which make up most of the Earth's atmosphere.
Check your answer.

Questions

1 Why is the Earth's atmosphere warming up?

2 Copy and comple the sentences, using these words:

   argon   nitrogen   carbon dioxide   oxygen

   80% of our atmosphere is _____ with the rest being mainly _____ .
   There is also a small amount of _____ which is a 'Greenhouse gas'.
   There are very small amounts of the noble gases. An example of a noble gas is _____ .

Module test questions

1   The diagram shows the rock cycle. Match words from the list with labels **1–4** on the diagram.

metamorphic
igneous
magma
sedimentary

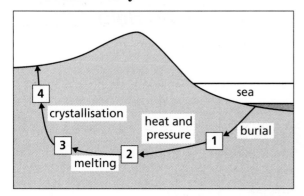

2   The table gives some information about four materials.
Match words from the list with the numbers **1–4** in the table.

concrete
slaked lime
quicklime
calcium carbonate

	Information about the material
1	made by a chemical reaction between cement and other materials
2	the main chemical in limestone
3	produced when you heat (roast) limestone
4	made by adding calcium oxide and water together

3   This question is about the uses of some materials found in crude oil. Match words from the list with numbers **1–4** in the table.

bitumen
fuel oil
gasoline (petrol)
kerosene

	The use of the material
1	used to surface roads
2	used as a fuel for cars
3	used as a fuel in aeroplanes
4	used as a fuel in ships

4   This question is about some of the gases in our atmosphere.
Match words from the list with numbers **1–4** in the table.

carbon dioxide
sulphur dioxide
oxygen
nitrogen

	Information about the gas
1	This gas represents about 20% of the atmosphere
2	This gas causes the Greenhouse Effect
3	This gas helps to cause acid rain
4	This gas represents about 80% of the atmosphere

5   Which *two* of the following are heated with sand to make glass?

A   quicklime
B   soda
C   limestone
D   slaked lime
E   clay.

6 Which *two* of the following are true of large hydrocarbons when compared to smaller hydrocarbons?
Larger hydrocarbons:

A have a higher melting point
B flow very easily (less viscous)
C are easier to evaporate
D are more reactive
E are less easy to ignite (burn less easily).

7 This is a diagram of the structure of the Earth.

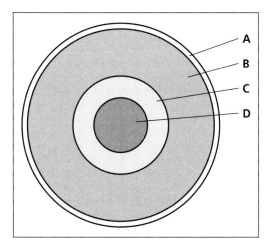

1. Which letter represents the crust?

A   B   C   D

2. Which letter represents the mantle?

A   B   C   D

3. Which letter represents the part of the Earth likely to be the most dense?

A   B   C   D

4. Which letter represents the area where convection currents are taking place? (These currents cause the movement of the Earth's plates.)

A   B   C   D

8 This is a diagram of a volcano erupting.

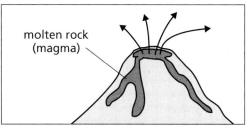

molten rock (magma)

1. An example of molten rock which could come from the volcano would be:

A sandstone
B limestone
C basalt
D marble.

2. If the rock cools slowly below the Earth's surface it is:

A extrusive igneous rock with small crystals
B extrusive igneous rock with large crystals
C intrusive igneous rock with small crystals
D intrusive igneous rock with large crystals.

3. Magma on the Earth's surface can become sedimentary rock if it:

A becomes buried and erupts again onto the surface
B wears away and is put under heat and pressure
C becomes buried, melts to form magma, then cools below the surface
D wears away and the grains become cemented together.

4. An example of an intrusive igneous rock is:

A marble
B sandstone
C mudstone
D granite.

Speeding up chemical reactions

You can increase the speed chemicals react with each other by doing any of these things:

- increase temperature

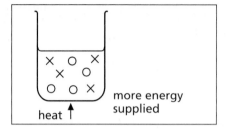

- increase the concentration of the reacting chemicals

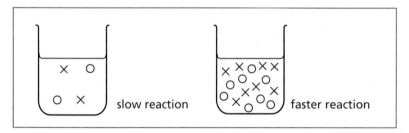

- increase the surface area of one of the reacting chemicals (by cutting it into smaller pieces)

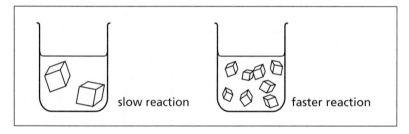

- increase the pressure on the reacting chemicals (when these are gases).

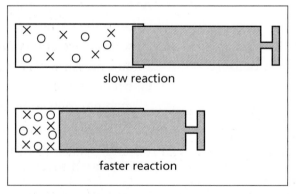

 *Checkpoint*

Cover the page, then write down the different ways of increasing the rate (speed) of a reaction.
Check your answer.

Catalysts

You can also use a catalyst. A catalyst speeds up a reaction but is not used up itself. It can be used over and over again. Different reactions need different catalysts.

The speed of a reaction is called the **rate of reaction**.

Chemicals react only when the particles bump into each other (collide) with enough energy. The minimum amount of energy you need to start a reaction is called the **activation energy**.

Increasing the temperature, concentration or pressure on reacting chemicals means they collide more often and with more energy. This is why the reaction speeds up.

In industry, increasing the rate of reaction can mean making more money.

Checkpoint

Cover the page, then write down what is meant by 'activation energy'.
Check your answer.

Has the reaction been speeded up?

You can measure the rate of reaction in different ways.
You can:

- measure the rate at which products are formed (e.g. the amount of gas given off)
- measure how fast the reacting chemicals are used up.

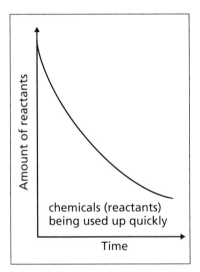

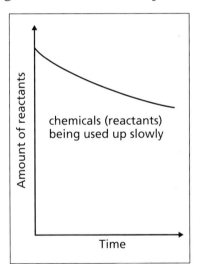

Measuring how quickly reactants are used up

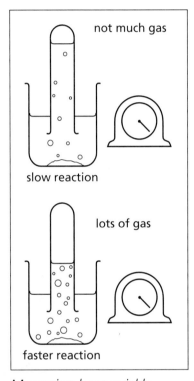

Measuring how quickly products are produced

Questions

1   Why does increasing the concentration of reacting chemicals increase the rate of reaction?

2   Copy and complete the sentences, choosing words from this list:

  increase   greater   collide   decrease   less

  You may _____ the rate of a reaction if you increase the temperature. This is because the particles _____ more often and with _____ energy.

3   How might you tell that a reaction has speeded up?

Useful chemical reactions

The production of fertiliser

Fertiliser is made so that farmers can replace the nutrients plants take up from the soil. This means that farmers can grow more crops. However, sometimes these fertilisers cause problems because they get washed out of the soil into rivers, ponds and lakes when it rains. Some get into our drinking water.

Ammonium nitrate fertiliser is made in the following way:

Stage 1   **Production of ammonia (the Haber process)**

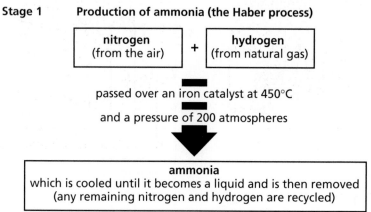

| nitrogen (from the air) | **+** | hydrogen (from natural gas) |

passed over an iron catalyst at 450°C

and a pressure of 200 atmospheres

ammonia
which is cooled until it becomes a liquid and is then removed
(any remaining nitrogen and hydrogen are recycled)

Stage 2   **Production of nitric acid**

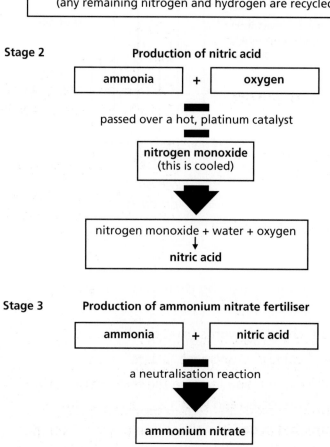

| ammonia | **+** | oxygen |

passed over a hot, platinum catalyst

nitrogen monoxide
(this is cooled)

nitrogen monoxide + water + oxygen
↓
nitric acid

Stage 3   **Production of ammonium nitrate fertiliser**

| ammonia | **+** | nitric acid |

a neutralisation reaction

ammonium nitrate

Living organisms and chemical reactions

Living cells use chemical reactions to produce new materials. Humans use yeast and bacteria to produce substances that they want.

Yeast cells convert (change) sugar into carbon dioxide and alcohol.

This process is called fermentation and it is used:

* to produce alcohol in wine and beer
* to produce carbon dioxide bubbles to make bread rise.

Bacteria are used to make yoghurt from milk. They change the lactose sugar in the milk into lactic acid.

Products using fermentation

These reactions take place faster when it is warm but not hot. Living organisms use enzymes as catalysts. Enzymes are proteins, which are usually damaged by temperatures above about 45°C.

Do chemical reactions release heat (energy)?

The answer is that some do and some don't.

An **exothermic** reaction releases energy, often as heat, which will warm up the surroundings. This happens when you burn a fuel.

An **endothermic** reaction results in energy, often as heat, being taken from the surroundings.

Help

Exothermic – heat given off.
Endothermic – heat taken in.

Checkpoint

Cover the page, then write down what you understand by the word 'exothermic'. Check your answer.

Questions

1 Name the *two* catalysts needed in the production of ammonium nitrate.

2 Why do enzymes make a reaction go faster at 30°C and stop working at 45°C?

3 Yeast is very useful to humans. Draw a spider diagram to show *three* useful substances which yeast helps us make. Put **yeast** at the centre of your diagram.

Chemical calculations

These are easy when you know how! To work out what is happening in chemical reactions we need to know the masses of the chemicals involved. We work this out by using **relative atomic masses** (A_r).

You will find relative atomic masses in the data book in the exam. These make it possible to work out the **relative formula mass** (M_r) of a compound.

Atoms of different elements have different relative atomic masses. For example:

$^{39}_{19}$K potassium $^{35}_{17}$Cl chlorine
A_r = 39 A_r = 35

You must be able to calculate the relative formula mass (M_r) of a compound if you are given its formula.

Help

To work out M_r – add up all of the relative atomic masses in a compound.

 Worked example

Q What is the M_r of carbon dioxide (CO_2)?

The relative atomic mass of carbon is 12
the relative atomic mass of oxygen is 16

A_r of carbon   = 12
A_r of oxygen   = 32 (there are two and each has a mass of 16)
        M_r = 44

 Worked example

Q What is the M_r of sulphuric acid (H_2SO_4)?

The relative atomic mass of hydrogen is 1
the relative atomic mass of oxygen is 16
the relative atomic mass of sulphur is 32

A_r of hydrogen =   2 (there are two and each has a mass of 1)
A_r of sulphur = 32
A_r of oxygen = 64 (there are four and each has a mass of 16)
        M_r = 98

Help

The relative atomic mass (A_r) is the top number.
e.g. $^{16}_{8}$O – the relative atomic mass is 16.

You must also be able to work out the percentage of an element in a compound.

Worked example

Q What is the percentage of carbon in carbon dioxide (CO_2)?

$$M_r \text{ of carbon dioxide} = 44$$
$$A_r \text{ of carbon} = 12$$
$$\% \text{ of carbon} = \frac{12}{44} \times 100$$
$$= 27.3\%$$

Worked example

Q What is the percentage of nitrogen in nitric acid (HNO_3)?

Work out the relative formula mass (M_r) of nitric acid first.

$$A_r \text{ of hydrogen} = 1$$
$$A_r \text{ of nitrogen} = 14$$
$$A_r \text{ of oxygen} = 48 \quad \text{(there are three oxygens each with a mass of 16)}$$
$$M_r = 63$$

the percentage
of nitrogen $= \dfrac{14 \times 100}{63}$

$$= 22.2\%$$

Questions

1 Work out the relative formula mass (M_r) for each of these compounds:
 a calcium carbonate ($CaCO_3$)
 b magnesium sulphate ($MgSO_4$)

2 What is the percentage of:
 a sodium in sodium chloride (NaCl)
 b sulphur in sulphur dioxide (SO_2)?

Relative atomic masses (A_r)	
carbon (C)	12
calcium (Ca)	40
chlorine (Cl)	35
magnesium (Mg)	24
sodium (Na)	23
oxygen (O)	16

In the laboratory

Safety symbols

There are some diagrams and symbols that you should be able to recognise in an examination.

oxidising
provide oxygen which allows other materials to burn more fiercely

toxic
can cause death when swallowed or breathed in or absorbed through the skin

corrosive
attack and destroy living tissues including eyes and skin

highly flammable
catch fire easily

harmful
similar to toxic substances but less dangerous

irritant
not corrosive but can cause reddening or blistering of the skin

You must also be able to name one hazardous (dangerous) substance (e.g. sulphuric acid).

Apparatus

You should be able to draw diagrams of chemical apparatus:

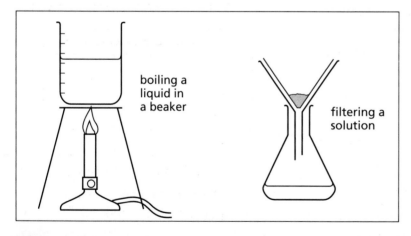

boiling a liquid in a beaker

filtering a solution

Help

Simple tests
There are some tests which can be carried out for various substances. For example:
Hydrogen burns with a squeaky 'pop'.
Carbon dioxide bubbled though lime water turns the lime water milky.
Chlorine gas bleaches damp litmus paper.

Questions

1a What is meant by 'flammable'?

b Name *one* substance that is highly flammable.

2 Describe *three* ways that a toxic substance might get into the body.

3a What are the uses of a filter funnel and a Bunsen burner?

b How would you use a filter funnel?

Terminal exam questions

1   Here are some drawings of chemical equipment.

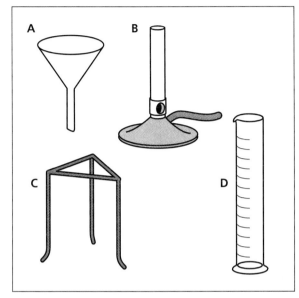

Name each piece of equipment and explain one use for it   [8]

[8 marks]

2 a   Suggest *three* ways of increasing the rate of a chemical reaction.
For each one explain why it speeds up the reaction.   [9]

  b   What is meant by the term 'activation energy'?   [2]

[11 marks]

3 a i Copy and complete the following sentences about the production of ammonium nitrate. Use words from the list to fill spaces 1–4.

  nitric acid
  hydrogen
  oxygen
  nitrogen

The gases ___1___ and ___2___ are reacted together to produce ammonia. This ammonia is now reacted with ___3___ to produce nitrogen dioxide. Nitrogen dioxide is reacted with oxygen and water to produce ___4___. This product is now reacted with the ammonia to produce ammonium nitrate.   [4]

  ii At what temperature and pressure is ammonia produced?   [2]

  iii What catalyst is used for the reaction?   [1]

  b   What problem can ammonium nitrate cause in the environment?   [4]

  c   What is meant by the term 'endothermic reaction'?   [2]

[13 marks]

4 a   You will need the following information to answer this question.

Relative atomic masses (A_r)	
hydrogen	1
oxygen	16
carbon	12
calcium	40

What are the relative formula masses (M_r) of:

  i ethanoic acid, CH_3COOH [4]

  ii calcium hydroxide, $Ca(OH)_2$?   [4]

  b   What is the percentage of:

  i oxygen in water, H_2O [3]

  ii carbon in calcium carbonate, $CaCO_3$?   [3]

[14 marks]

Total for test: 46 marks

Solids, liquids and gases

All of these are made up of very small particles.

Solids have a definite shape and a definite volume (that is, they take up a set amount of space). The particles are very close together. They cannot move much but only vibrate (in a very small area). This is why solids have definite shape.

Liquids have a definite volume but no definite shape. The particles are quite close together but can move around (slide past each other). This means they can be poured. It also means they take the shape of any container they are poured into.

Gases have no definite shape or volume. They can spread out into a big space and they can be squeezed (compressed) into a small space. The particles are not very close together and can move around a lot. This is why gases are very light.

Checkpoint

Cover the page, then write down how a solid is different from a liquid, in terms of the particles.
Check your answer.

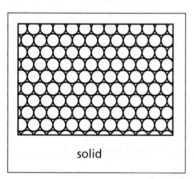

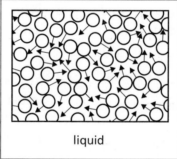

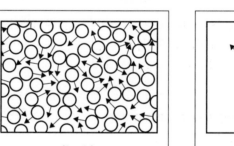

solid   liquid   gas

Substances can exist in three states

Melting points and boiling points

Solids can become liquids. Liquids can become gases. You have to supply energy to do this. If you take energy away then gases can become liquids and then solids.

If energy (heat) is supplied to a solid, the particles move about more. The solid may melt (that is, become a liquid). The temperature it melts at is called its **melting point**.

If even more energy is supplied, this liquid may boil. The temperature it boils at is its **boiling point**.

If you give the particles in a liquid enough energy to overcome the forces of attraction to the other particles, then they escape and form a gas. This is called **evaporation**. The higher the temperature, the faster the evaporation. This happens at boiling point and beyond.

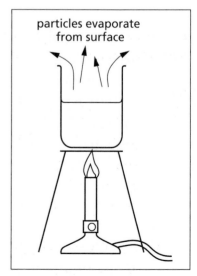

Evaporation

Diffusion

The particles of a gas move in all directions. Gases spread out in the space they are in. After a time they are evenly spread out in the space. This is called **diffusion**.

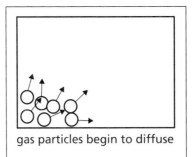
gas particles begin to diffuse

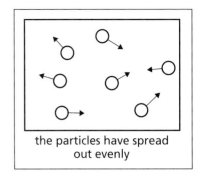
the particles have spread out evenly

Dissolving

As the particles in a liquid move they can sometimes bump into particles of a solid and knock them apart. This happens if you add salt to water or sugar to a cup of tea. The particles of the solid then move through the liquid particles by diffusion. This is called **dissolving**.

Atoms

The particles in solids, liquids and gases are made of atoms. There are over 90 sorts. Some of the atoms you will come across include sodium, oxygen and chlorine.

Atoms have a small nucleus. The nucleus contains protons and neutrons. Whizzing around the nucleus are electrons.

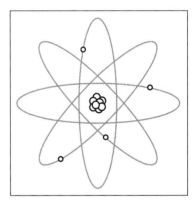

	Mass	Charge
proton	1	+1 (positive)
neutron	1	0 (neutral)
electron	almost 0	–1 (negative)

Atoms have no overall charge (they are neutral). They have the same number of protons and electrons.

 *Checkpoint*

Cover the page, then write down the charge of a proton, a neutron and an electron. Check your answer.

 Questions

1 Copy and complete the table using these words:

liquid   solid   gas

State	Properties
	easy to pour
	diffuses to fill all of the space
	particles are hardly free to move at all

2 If you know the number of protons in an atom, you also know the number of electrons. Why?

More about atoms

Protons and neutrons

All atoms of the same element have the same number of protons. For example:

- all sodium atoms have 11 protons
- all oxygen atoms have 8 protons
- all chlorine atoms have 17 protons.

All elements have different numbers of protons. For example, only sodium has 11 protons – no other element.

The number of protons is the **proton number** (or the **atomic number**).

The number of protons plus the number of neutrons is the **mass number**.

Every element has a symbol (e.g. Na is the symbol for sodium). When you write it down, you can also put the mass number at the top and the atomic or proton number at the bottom of the symbol. For example:

$$\text{mass number} \rightarrow {}^{23}_{11}\text{Na} \text{ (sodium)}$$
$$\text{proton number} \rightarrow$$

Isotopes

Atoms of the same element may have different numbers of neutrons. These atoms are called **isotopes** of that element.

Electrons

The electrons are whizzing around the nucleus of an atom in 'orbits'. These are called **electron shells**. The shell closest to the nucleus is at the lowest energy level. This means that the electrons here need less energy to stay in orbit than those in any other shells. The further away from the nucleus, the higher the energy level. The electrons in any atom are always found as close as possible to the nucleus.

The first shell (nearest to the nucleus) holds a maximum of two electrons.

The next shells can hold up to eight electrons each.

You can write down an atom's **electronic structure**. For example, sodium has 11 electrons arranged like this: sodium 2, 8, 1.

Help

Isotopes still have the same number of protons, because they are the same element.

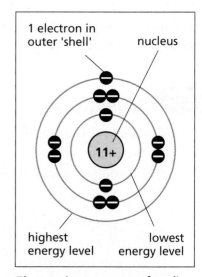

Electronic structure of sodium

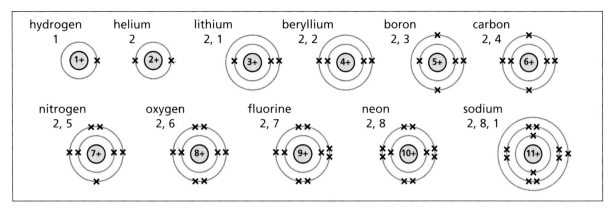

Electronic structures of the first 11 elements in the periodic table

Compounds and chemical bonds

Most substances are compounds formed from two or more atoms. These are held together with chemical bonds. There are two types of chemical bond – ionic and covalent.

Ionic bonds

An ionic bond forms when one of the atoms in a compound gains one or more electrons, and another atom loses one or more electrons. The atoms now have a charge and are called ions. The compound is an ionic compound.

An ionic compound is a giant structure of ions. These compounds have high melting and boiling points because the bonds formed are strong.

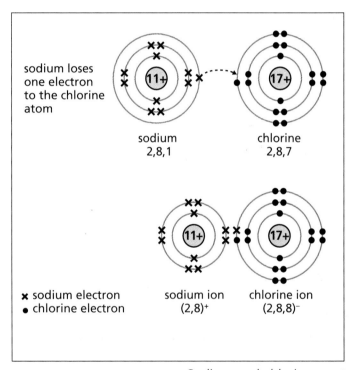

Sodium and chlorine react

Questions

1 Magnesium is shown as: $^{24}_{12}$Mg
   a What is its proton number?   c How many electrons are there?
   b What is its mass number?   d What is the electronic structure of magnesium?

2 Oxygen has an electronic structure of 2, 6. Draw a diagram of how magnesium and oxygen form an ionic bond.

3 Look at the diagram at the top of this page. Draw a similar diagram of the electronic structures of elements 12 to 20.

More about chemical bonds

When atoms form compounds their outer electron shells become full. Atoms like to have full outer shells. They can do this by gaining or losing electrons when making ionic bonds. Atoms can also share elecrons to form covalent bonds.

Covalent bonds

In covalent bonds the atoms share electrons. They don't gain or lose any.

Atoms which share electrons form molecules. There are bonds between the atoms *in* a molecule but not *between* molecules. So substances made of molecules usually have low melting and boiling points, because the molecules separate very easily. Molecular compounds are often liquids or gases at room temperature.

Help

Atoms which share electrons can also form giant structures.

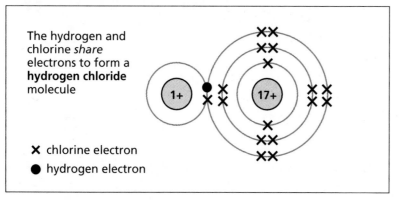

The hydrogen and chlorine *share* electrons to form a **hydrogen chloride** molecule

✗ chlorine electron
● hydrogen electron

A molecule of hydrogen chloride

The periodic table

We group the elements into families. They can be arranged in order of their proton (atomic) number. This means that they are also arranged in terms of their electronic structure.

The list is arranged so that elements with the same number of electrons in their outer shells are in the same columns or groups. So, for example, the elements in group 1 (e.g. sodium, potassium, lithium) all have only one electron in the outer shell.

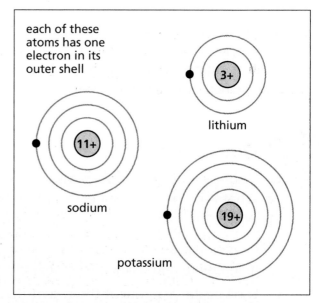

each of these atoms has one electron in its outer shell

lithium

sodium

potassium

Similar elements can be grouped

groups											
I	II										
H											He
Li	Be						B	C	N	O	F	Ne
Na	Mg						Al	Si	P	S	Cl	Ar
K	Ca	transition metals									

Part of the periodic table

The history of the periodic table

For a long time chemists searched to find patterns which might explain and predict the behaviour of elements. Around 1800, John Dalton introduced the idea that chemical elements were made up of atoms, and that atoms of different elements had different masses. Thirty years later, another chemist showed that elements could be grouped into threes, or 'triads' (e.g. lithium, sodium and potassium).

In 1863, John Newlands came up with the idea of arranging elements in order of their atomic masses in groups of eight, or 'octaves'. A few years later, Mendeléev published the first clear table grouping elements by their atomic masses and properties. Not all of the elements were known at the time, so this early table had gaps. When elements were eventually found which fitted the gaps, it strengthened belief in the table.

Question

1   Copy and complete the sentences, choosing words from this list:

   sharing   high   low   atoms   exchanging   molecule

Two oxygen _____ join together to form an oxygen molecule (O_2). The bond is formed by _____ electrons. Oxygen is covalent. Covalent compounds tend to have _____ melting and boiling points.

Groups in the periodic table

Group 1 elements

These are called the **alkali metals** because when they react with water they produce an alkaline solution. They include lithium (Li), sodium (Na) and potassium (K).

The alkali metals:

- have the properties of all metals

- react with non-metals to form ionic compounds – their ions carry a 1+ charge (because they lose their outer electron)

- react with water giving off hydrogen and forming an hydroxide – this dissolves in the water to form an alkaline solution.

When placed in cold water, the metal floats and often moves around on the surface. The more reactive the metal, the more vigorous its reaction with water.

The further down the group the metal is:

- the lower its melting point and boiling point

- the more reactive it is.

So potassium is more reactive than sodium, which is more reactive than lithium.

Group 7 elements (the halogens)

These include fluorine (F), chlorine (Cl) and bromine (Br).

The halogens:

- are all non-metals

- as gases, all have coloured vapours (chlorine is green, bromine is brown)

- consist of molecules which are pairs of atoms (e.g. Cl_2, Br_2)

- form ionic salts in which the chloride, bromide or fluoride ion carries one negative charge, such as Na^+Br^- (sodium bromide)

- form molecular compounds with other non-metals, for example:

$$C + 2Cl_2 \rightarrow CCl_4 \text{ (tetrachloromethane)}$$

Checkpoint

Cover the page. Can you remember how many electrons group 1 metals have in their outer shell? Check your answer.

Help

Group 1 metals and group 7 non-metals react so well together because the metal has to *lose one electron* (to make a full outer shell) and the non-metal has to *gain one electron*.

Group 0 elements (the noble gases)

These are at the very right-hand side of the periodic table. They all have 8 electrons in their outer shell (which is why they are sometimes called group 8 elements). They include helium (He), neon (Ne) and argon (Ar).

Help

Noble gases are unreactive because they don't need to lose or gain electrons to get a full outer shell.

The noble gases:

• are very unreactive

• exist as single atoms (e.g. Ne)

• are used as inert (unreactive) gases in light bulbs and electrical discharge tubes – they glow with different coloured light (you may have heard of 'neon' lights).

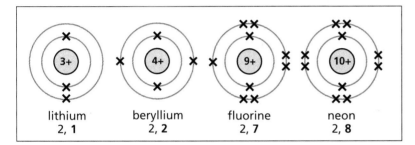

lithium	beryllium	fluorine	neon
2, 1	2, 2	2, 7	2, 8

Some elements from groups 1, 2, 7 and 0

The transition metals

These appear in the centre of the periodic table. They include iron (Fe) and copper (Cu).

The transition metals:

• have high melting points

• are often used as catalysts (e.g. in the Haber process)

• form coloured compounds (e.g. iron oxide, which is rust).

Questions

1   Give *three* properties of the halogen gases.

2   Neon has an electronic structure of 2, 8. Why is it so unreactive?

3   Why does a group 1 element have a 1+ charge when it becomes an ion?

Useful halides

The halogens (group 7 elements) produce many useful salts. These salts are called **halides**. One of the most useful is sodium chloride.

Using sodium chloride

Sodium chloride (salt) is made when sodium and chlorine join to form an ionic compound. It is found in large amounts in the sea and underground.

The electrolysis of sodium chloride solution (brine) is an important industrial process. Sodium chloride dissolved in water produces four ions:

- positive sodium ions (Na^+) and negative chloride ions (Cl^-) from the salt ($NaCl$), and

- positive hydrogen ions (H^+) and negative hydroxide ions (OH^-) from the water (H_2O).

When electricity is passed through the solution:

- chloride ions (negative) move to the positive electrode, and chlorine gas is given off

- positive hydrogen ions move to the negative electrode, and hydrogen gas is given off

- a solution of sodium hydroxide ($NaOH$) is left behind.

Help

When two elements are attached by strong bonds then a lot of energy is needed to separate them.

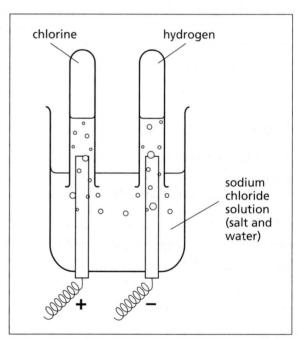

The electrolysis of sodium chloride solution

What happens at the electrodes?

Chloride ions (Cl^-) arrive at the positive electrode. An electron is lost from each chloride ion to leave it neutral again (in other words, to leave it as a chlorine atom again):

$$Cl^- - e^- \rightarrow Cl$$

But you need two chlorine atoms to make a molecule of chlorine gas, so:

$$2Cl^- - 2e^- \rightarrow Cl_2$$

This chlorine gas is given off. A test for chlorine is that it bleaches damp litmus paper.

What are the substances produced used for?

Chlorine is used to kill bacteria in drinking water and swimming pools – it is also used in disinfectants and bleach. The plastic PVC is a polymer made with chlorine.

Hydrogen is used in the manufacture of ammonia (for fertiliser) and margarine.

 *Checkpoint*

Cover the page, then write down *two* uses of chlorine and *two* uses of hydrogen. Check your answer.

Sodium hydroxide is used in the manufacture of soap, paper and ceramics.

More uses for the halides

Hydrogen halides (e.g. hydrogen chloride, HCl) are gases that dissolve in water to produce acidic solutions (e.g. hydrochloric acid, H^+Cl^-).

Metal halides are used in the production of photographs. Silver chloride, silver bromide and silver iodide are reduced to silver by the action of light, X-rays and radiation. They are used to make photographic film and photographic paper.

 Questions

1   This question is about the electrolysis of sodium chloride solution. Copy and complete the sentences, using these words:

    chlorine   electron   chloride   positive

    In the electrolysis of sodium chloride negative _____ ions move to the _____ electrode. The ions then lose an _____ . The ions become atoms. Two atoms join to become a _____ molecule.

2   State *two* uses of silver halides.

3   When sodium chloride solution is electrolysed useful substances are produced. Draw a spider diagram to show these useful substances. Put **sodium chloride** at the centre of your diagram.

Symbols, formulae and equations

Chemical symbols, formulae and equations can look
complicated – but they are only a form of useful shorthand
to describe compounds and how they can change.

Chemical symbols

There are over 90 elements known to us
today. They are all shown in the periodic
table. The ten you are most likely to
come across are listed here.

Every element has its own symbol, so
instead of writing out the name of the
element you can use its symbol.

Element	Symbol
hydrogen	H
carbon	C
nitrogen	N
oxygen	O
sodium	Na

Element	Symbol
magnesium	Mg
sulphur	S
chlorine	Cl
potassium	K
calcium	Ca

Formulae

Compounds are made from a number of elements. These
can be shown by chemical formulae, which show the
atoms in the compounds and how many of them there are.
For example:

- carbon dioxide is shown as CO_2 – which means that
  each molecule has one atom of carbon and two atoms
  of oxygen

- sodium chloride is NaCl – which means that for every
  one atom of sodium there is one of chlorine

- water is H_2O – which means that for every two atoms of
  hydrogen there is one of oxygen.

Ionic compounds

These are compounds made up of positively and
negatively charged ions. They are usually the salts of
metals or hydrogen. You can work out their formulae if
you know the charge on the ions.

Help

In the exam you will be
able to find the charges on
all the ions you need. They
are in the data book.

 Worked example

Q What is the formula of the ionic compound calcium chloride?

A A calcium ion has two positive charges (Ca^{2+}) and a chloride ion
has one negative charge (Cl^-).

So each calcium ion needs two chloride ions to balance its
positive charges. Therefore calcium chloride is $CaCl_2$.

Other compounds

You need to know the formulae of some other common covalent compounds. These are shown in the table.

Covalent compound	Formula
carbon dioxide	CO_2
sulphur dioxide	SO_2
ammonia	NH_3
nitrogen monoxide	NO
nitrogen dioxide	NO_2

Equations

Equations show us what is happening during a chemical reaction. The elements or compounds at the start of a reaction (the **reactants**) are shown on the left of the arrow. The substances they produce are shown on the right (the **products**).

For example, this word equation shows a neutralisation reaction (when an acid and an alkali form a salt and water):

State	Symbol
solid	s
liquid	l
gas	g
aqueous solution (dissolved in water)	aq

$$\text{sodium hydroxide} + \text{hydrochloric acid} \rightarrow \text{sodium chloride} + \text{water}$$

reactants · products

The symbol equation is:

$$NaOH + HCl \rightarrow NaCl + H_2O$$

This word equation shows another way of forming a metal salt:

$$\text{calcium} + \text{hydrochloric acid} \rightarrow \text{calcium chloride} + \text{hydrogen}$$

and can be shown using chemical symbols:

$$Ca + 2HCl \rightarrow CaCl_2 + H_2$$

If state symbols are added (see table above) the equation looks like this:

$$Ca(s) + 2HCl(l) \rightarrow CaCl_2(s) + H_2(g)$$

Help

Do not worry about the '2' in front of HCl. This is there to balance the equation (by making sure that there are the same number of atoms on each side). You need to understand chemical equations, but you will not have to balance them.

Questions

1 Work out the formulae for the following compounds. Use the information in the table and on these pages to help you.

Ion	Formula
sodium	Na^+
magnesium	Mg^{2+}
hydroxide	OH^-
oxide	O^{2-}

a sodium hydroxide
b magnesium oxide
c sodium oxide
d magnesium chloride.

2 The symbol equations below are found in the chemistry sections of your science syllabus. For each one write the equation as a word equation.

a $2Mg + O_2 \rightarrow 2MgO$ b $2K + 2H_2O \rightarrow 2KOH + H_2$ c $2Na + Cl_2 \rightarrow 2NaCl$

Terminal exam questions

1 a i Copy and complete the boxes to show the arrangement of particles in a solid, liquid and a gas. The solid has been drawn for you. [2]

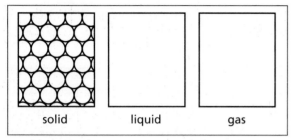

solid   liquid   gas

ii What happens when a solid melts (in terms of the particles)? [3]

iii Why do liquids evaporate more quickly if you heat them to a higher temperature? [2]

b What is meant by the term 'diffusion'? [3]

[10 marks]

2 Sodium can be represented as $^{23}_{11}$Na.

a i How many protons has sodium? [1]

ii How many electrons has sodium? [1]

iii How many neutrons has sodium? [1]

iv What is the atomic mass of sodium? [1]

b Sodium has the electron structure 2, 8, 1.
Copy and complete the diagram to show this structure. [2]

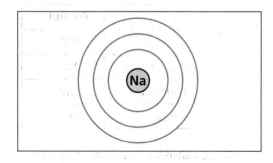

c i Potassium (2, 8, 8, 1) reacts violently with fluorine (2, 7).
Copy and complete the diagrams to show how this happens. [3]

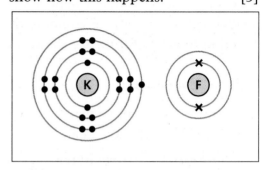

ii What type of bond is formed? [1]

[10 marks]

3 This is part of the periodic table.

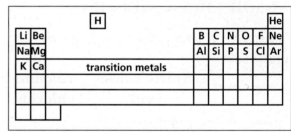

a i Shade the group 2 metals. [1]

ii Name *two* of the elements shown in group 1. [2]

iii Name the *two* elements shown in group 7. [2]

b Why are the elements in group 0 so unreactive? [2]

[7 marks]

Total for test: 27 marks

AT4
Physical Processes

Energy

Electricity

Forces

Waves and Radiation

The transfer of heat

There are three different ways that heat can be transferred – conduction, convection and radiation.

Conduction

If one part of a metal bar is hot and the other part cool, then heat is transferred to the cooler part. The metal does not move. If one end of a piece of wood is hot and the other end is cool, the heat does not transfer very quickly at all. This is because metals are good **conductors** of heat and non-metals (like wood) are poor conductors of heat.

A material which conducts heat very poorly is called an **insulator**.

Convection

Liquids and gases can move. They can transfer heat because they move. A good example of this would be a heater in a room.

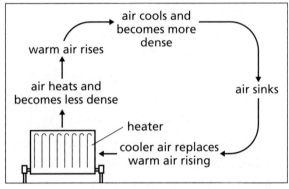

Convection

Radiation

This is the transfer of energy (heat) through empty space. If you stand in the Sun it heats you up. This cannot be conduction as there is no solid connection between you and the Sun. It cannot be convection as there are no gases or liquids between the Earth and the Sun. Hot bodies, like the Sun, give off infrared radiation.

The hotter the body, the more radiation is given off (emitted).

Dark, dull surfaces emit a lot of radiation. They also absorb a lot of radiation. Shiny, white surfaces are poor emitters of radiation and do not absorb much either.

 *Help*

Conduction – only through solids.

Convection – by liquids and gases.

Radiation – can pass through space.

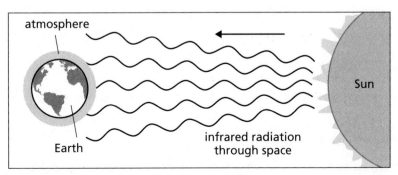

Radiation from the Sun

 **Just think!**

White houses and cars in Spain, and white clothes worn in Arabian countries, help keep people cool.

Using insulation

The ideas of heat loss and insulation can be used to prevent heat loss from a house.

Most ways of insulating a house are based on the fact that air is a very poor conductor of heat. They include:

- double glazing – traps a layer of air between two panes of glass
- fibreglass lagging in the roof – traps air within the layers of fibreglass
- cavity walls – the gaps between the bricks are filled with air
- cavity wall insulation – foam in the cavity traps air, so it cannot rise (by convection) even when it warms up.
- draught excluder – strips of foam around a door frame make a tight-fitting door, so warm air cannot escape.

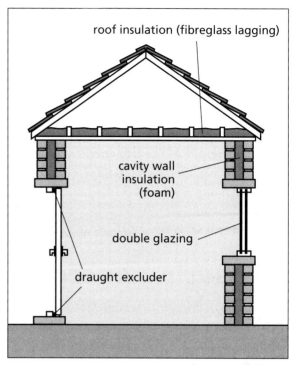

Reducing heat loss from a house

Gravitational potential energy

Energy has different forms, including heat and electricity. Another is **gravitational potential energy**. This is the energy stored in an object which has been lifted. For example, if a crane lifts a steel girder the gravitational potential energy of the girder has increased because it has gained height.

Questions

1 Copy and complete the sentences using these words:

      conduction   insulation   radiation   convection

The transfer of heat through a solid is known as _____ . If the transfer of the heat can take place through space this is known as _____ . A material which prevents heat loss is a form of _____ . The movement of gas or a liquid in heat loss is known as _____ .

2 Why are most cars in Spain white in colour?

3 Why does fibreglass lagging prevent heat loss through the roof of a house?

Using energy

Much of the energy used at home and work is transferred by electricity. Electrical energy is easily turned into heat, light, sound and movement.

Electrical appliances

Many household appliances are electric. These include:

- heaters (e.g. fan heaters, electric bar heaters)
- light (e.g. light bulbs, television)
- sound (e.g. radio, television, stereo systems)
- movement (e.g. food processors, hair driers).

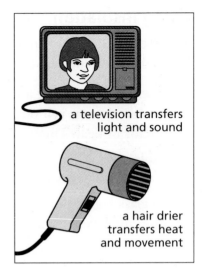

a television transfers light and sound

a hair drier transfers heat and movement

Measuring energy

We measure energy in joules (J). Power (watts) is a measure of how fast energy is transferred. The greater the power, the more energy is transferred in a given time – as shown in the formula:

$$\frac{\textbf{power}}{\text{(watt/W)}} = \frac{\textbf{energy transferred (joule/J)}}{\textbf{time taken (second/s)}}$$

You do not have to remember this formula, but must be able to use it.

1 watt is the transfer of 1 joule of energy in 1 second.

You can rearrange the formula to find out the amount of electrical energy transferred (used) by an appliance:

$$\begin{array}{ccc} \textbf{energy transferred} & = & \textbf{power} & \times & \textbf{time} \\ \text{(joule/J)} & & \text{(watt/W)} & & \text{(second/s)} \end{array}$$

You do not have to remember this formula, but must be able to use it..

 **Checkpoint**

Cover the page, then write down the units for power and energy.
Check your answer.

 Worked example

Q A hair drier transfers 10 000 J of energy in 80 s. What is the power rating of the hair drier?

A power = $\dfrac{\text{energy transferred}}{\text{time}}$

$= \dfrac{10\,000}{80}$

$= 125\,\text{W}$

How much does the electricity used cost?

This depends on how much the appliance uses (transfers). It will cost more the longer the appliance is switched on and the faster it transfers (uses) electricity – this depends on its power.

The power of an appliance is measured in watts (W) or kilowatts (kW). 1 kW is 1000 W. The energy transferred from the mains is measured in kilowatt hours (kWh), which are also called **units**. Electricity bills are costed in units.

Units are worked out using the same formula as before but using kW per hour not W per second:

energy transferred = power × time
(kilowatt hour/kWh) (kilowatt/kW) (hour/h)

To calculate the cost of the electricity use this formula:

total cost = number of units × cost per unit

You do not have to remember this formula, but must be able to use it.

For example, if you have used 434 units at 42p for each unit the cost will be:

434 units × 42p = £182.28

 **Help**

A 100 W light bulb is brighter than a 60 W light bulb because it is transferring (using) more electricity in the same time.

 Worked example

A fan heater has a rating of 2 kW. It is switched on for 90 minutes. How much energy is transferred?

energy transferred
= power × time
= 2 × 1.5
(90 minutes is 1.5 hours)
= 3 kilowatt hours

How efficient are appliances?

In all appliances some of the energy is used usefully – and some is wasted. For example:

- a hair drier – the useful energy is heat and movement (the fan), and some is wasted as noise energy
- an electric mixer – the useful energy is movement, and the wasted energy is noise and heat (it will warm up).

The wasted energy is usually lost. It is very difficult to 'capture' this wasted energy and it spreads out quickly – it cannot be used again.

 Questions

1 Draw a spider diagram to show at least *three* household appliances that transfer electricity to *useful* sound energy. Put **sound** at the centre of your diagram.

2 A microwave transfers 6000 J of energy in 8 s. What is its power rating?

Generating electricity

Electricity from the mains is produced (generated) in power stations. Energy from other sources is used to drive **turbines**, which drive **generators** to make electricity.

Most electricity is generated by heating water to produce steam to drive the turbines.

Heating water

Fossil fuels can be burned. These fuels include:

- coal
- oil
- gas.

Fossil fuels are **non-renewable fuels**. The more slowly we use them, the longer they will last.

Nuclear fuels

These are also non-renewable fuels. Nuclear power stations use radioactive uranium or plutonium for energy to heat water. However, when nuclear accidents occur radiation can be released into the environment. This is rare. Once the nuclear fuel has been used it is very expensive to get rid of (reprocess).

Renewable energy sources

Small amounts of electricity can be generated using **renewable** energy sources.

Wood can be burned to heat water to generate electricity. It is renewable because trees can grow again. However, wood produces less heat than the same amount of fossil fuel.

Wind farms

Wind turbines produce no chemical pollution. However, you need many wind turbines to produce a reasonable amount of electricity. They have to be built where there is plenty of wind (e.g. on hilltops), which can be an eyesore. It is difficult to control the supply of electricity because this depends on the amount of wind.

Tidal power

The rise and fall of sea level with the tides can be used to turn turbines and generate electricity. There is no chemical pollution, but turbines placed across estuaries can obstruct shipping. The supply of electricity is reliable because tides are regular and sea levels predictable.

Help

Fossil fuels are formed from the remains of living organisms which lived millions of years ago. Once they are used up, these fuels cannot be replaced.

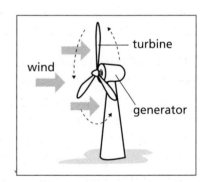

Wind power

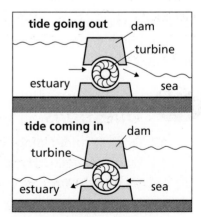

Tidal power

Hydroelectricity

These power stations can only be built where there is a ready supply of running water (e.g. mountain areas of Scotland). There is no chemical pollution, but reservoirs need to be made (often by damming rivers) to store water. This destroys wildlife. Electricity can be produced quickly and reliably by releasing water from the reservoir.

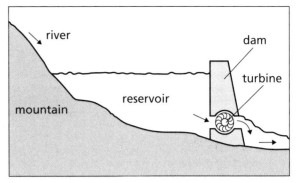

Hydroelectric power

Solar power

Light energy from the Sun can be used in two ways: in **solar panels** (to heat water) and in **solar cells** (to generate electricity). This is an expensive way of producing electricity but is worthwhile where there are no other sources available (e.g. very remote areas). There must be enough sunlight for the solar cells to work, but the electricity they generate can be stored in batteries (e.g. for use at night). There is no chemical pollution.

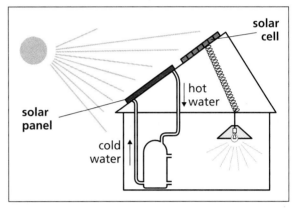

Solar power

Solar cells are used to power calculators. Some houses are fitted with cells and panels, but you would need a great number of them to generate enough power for large areas.

Hot rocks

Rocks deep below the surface of the Earth are hot because of decaying radioactive elements within them (similar to a nuclear power station!). They can be used to heat water to generate electricity. These power stations can be expensive to set up, but there is no chemical pollution. Producing electricity using energy from hot rocks is reliable because the rocks are always there and always hot.

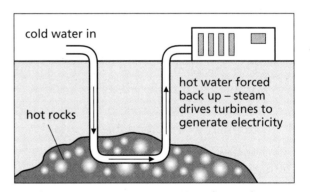

Geothermal power

 Questions

1 Draw a table with the headings **Non-renewable** and **Renewable**. Write at least *three* examples of energy sources in each column.

2 Suggest *two* advantages and *two* disadvantages of wind farms as a source of energy.

Module test questions

1 This question is about energy transfer. Match words from the list with the numbers **1–4** in the table.

radiation
insulation
conduction
convection

	Description
1	heat transfer through the movement of a gas
2	prevention of heat loss
3	heat transfer through a solid
4	heat transfer by waves

2 Match the symbols in the list with the spaces **1–4** to complete these sentences.

kWh J W s

The unit of power is _____1_____ .
The unit of energy is _____2_____ .
The unit of time is _____3_____ .
The unit for the costs of electricity is _____4_____ .

3 This question is about how household appliances transfer electrical energy. Match the appliances in the list to the numbers **1–4** in the table.

radio
toaster
torch
food mixer

	Description of energy transfer
1	electrical to movement
2	electrical to sound
3	electrical to heat
4	electrical to light

4 The table below describes different energy sources.
Match each of the sources in the list with the best description **1–4** in the table.

coal
uranium
solar
hydroelectric

	Description
1	the source for nuclear energy
2	burned to heat water
3	running water drives the turbines
4	converts energy directly from the Sun

5 Which *two* types of energy transfer best describe *useful* energy transfer by a television?

A movement
B heat
C light
D sound
E chemical.

6 Which *two* methods of electricity generation represent non-renewable energy sources?

A wind
B coal
C hydroelectric
D solar
E nuclear.

7 The diagram shows various forms of house insulation.

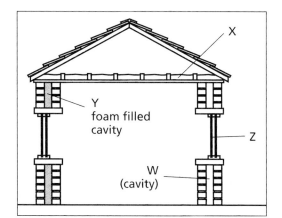

1. The insulation at X:

A prevents radiation of heat
B traps air and prevents convection
C is made of fibreglass, which prevents conduction
D is expensive and saves little money.

2. The insulation at Y is more effective than W because the foam:

A conducts heat through the wall
B prevents radiation of heat
C replaces air which is a good conductor
D prevents air rising, so reducing heat loss by convection.

3. The insulation at Z:

A is cheap and not effective
B is expensive and effective
C is expensive and not effective
D is cheap and effective.

4. Another good way of insulating the house would be to:

A replace thin curtains with thick ones
B leave doors open to let air circulate
C keep the house very warm
D control the temperature of all the radiators.

8 This is a hair drier.

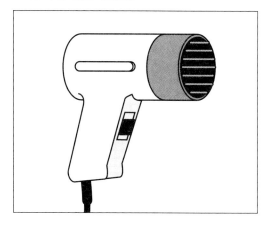

1. In which *two* of the following ways is energy usefully transferred?

A heat and sound
B light and heat
C heat and movement
D movement and sound.

2. One watt is the transfer of:

A one joule of energy in one minute
B one joule of energy in one second
C 1000 J of energy in one second
D 1000 J of energy in one minute.

3. This hair drier transfers 1000 J in 20 s. What is its power rating?
Use this equation:

$$\text{power} = \frac{\text{energy transferred}}{\text{time}}$$

A 0.2 W
B 50 W
C 0.5 W
D 200 W

4. An electricity bill is costed on the number of units you have used.
What is one unit?

A a watt hour
B a watt minute
C a kilowatt hour
D a kilowatt minute.

Electrical circuits

Electrical current flows through **circuits**. Current is a flow of electrons (**charge**). It transfers energy to **components** such as light bulbs, heaters and motors (e.g. in washing machines, hair driers, lawnmowers). Electrical current is measured in amperes (amps).

A circuit has a source of electrical power (e.g. a battery or mains electricity) and components.

Components resist the flow of electricity. **Resistance** is a measure of how easy or difficult it is for the current to flow.

Voltage

The electric current is 'pushed' around a circuit by the **voltage** of the power supply. (Voltage is also called **potential difference** or **p.d.**) A small battery is about 1.5 volts. A car battery is 12 volts. Mains electricity is 230 volts.

A battery is made up of **cells** connected in **series**. If you connect up two or more cells in series, the voltage they provide for a circuit is the sum (total) of all their voltages.

Circuits in series

If the components of a circuit are connected in series:

- the same amount of current flows through each component (the current has no alternative but to flow through all the components)
- the voltage (potential difference) of the electricity supply is shared between the components
- the resistance of the circuit is the resistance of each component added together.

Circuits in parallel

If the components are connected in **parallel:**

- the full voltage (p.d.) of the circuit goes through each component, but
- the current in the circuit 'splits' to travel through different components (current can flow most easily through the component with the smallest resistance)

Help

Potential difference is the difference in energy between two points in an electrical circuit. It is also called **voltage**.

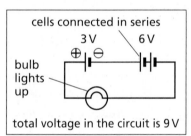

Cells connected in series

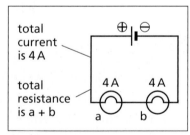

A circuit in series

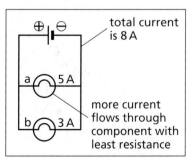

A circuit in parallel

- the total current in the whole circuit is the sum of the currents through the separate components
- the total resistance is the sum of the resistance of each component.

Circuit symbols

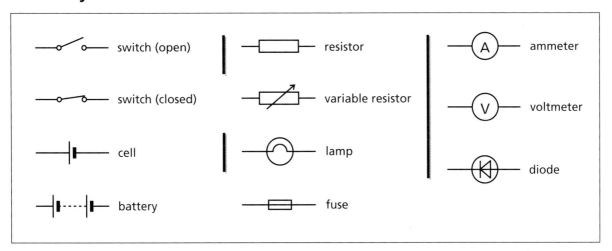

Electrolysis

If ionic compounds (e.g. common salt, NaCl) are melted or dissolved in water they conduct electricity. The current is caused by negatively charged ions (e.g. Cl^-) moving to the positive electrode, and positively charged ions (e.g. Na^+) moving to the negative electrode. Some of the elements in compounds are released at the electrodes. This is called **electrolysis**.

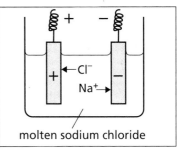

Electrolysis

 Questions

1 Here is a simple electrical circuit connected in series.
  a What is the component **X**?
  b What is the component **Y**?
  c What is the total current flowing?
  d If each cell is 3 V, what is the total p.d. (potential difference) of the circuit?
  e How much p.d. is there across each component?

2 Copy and complete these sentences, using words from this list:

  adding   components   cell   subtracting

  The current for the circuit is provided by a _____ . The total current in the circuit can be found by _____ the current flowing through the different _____ .

Power and resistance

Measuring current and voltage

You can measure the current (in amps) flowing through a component by using an **ammeter**. You must connect the ammeter in series with the component.

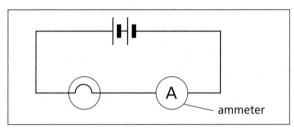

An ammeter is connected in series

You can measure voltage (potential difference) flowing across a component by using a voltmeter. This has to be connected to either side of the component (across the component).

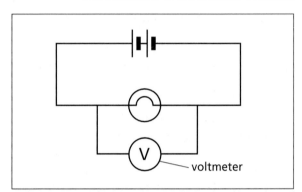

A voltmeter is connected across the component

Working out power

Once you know the current and voltage flowing through and across a component, you can work out how much energy is being transferred to the appliance. Multiply voltage by current and you have the amount of energy being transferred every second. This measurement is the **power rating** and is given in watts.

The rate of energy transfer is shown by this formula.

power = **potential difference** × **current**
(watt/W)   (volt/V)   (ampere/A)

All appliances have a power rating. For example, light bulbs can be 100 W, 60 W or 40 W.

Worked example

Q An electric drill has a current flowing through it of 3 A. It is connected to the mains supply (230 V). What is the power rating of the drill?

A power = potential difference × current
         = 230 × 3
         = 690 W

Resistance

All electrical appliances or components in a circuit resist the current. The bigger this **resistance,** the less current flows through the appliance. In other words, you need a bigger voltage (push) to get the same amount of current through the component.

In some components (e.g. light bulbs) the resistance increases as the voltage increases. This is because, as the filament heats up, it gets more resistant. The increase in the current flowing through the component is therefore smaller.

Current–voltage graphs show how current through a component varies with the voltage across it.

For example:

- as the voltage increases through a *resistor* so does the current – at a *constant* rate

- as the voltage increases through a *filament* so does the current – but at higher values the current does not increase so much

- when the voltage is reversed through a *diode* only a very small current flows – a diode allows current through in *one direction*.

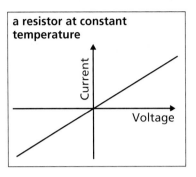

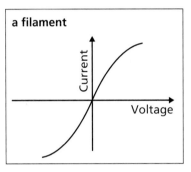

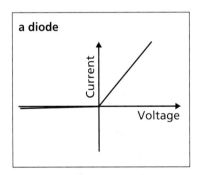

Current–voltage graphs

Questions

1 An electric saw is plugged into the mains (230 V). A current of 5 A flows through it. What is the power rating of the saw?

2 Copy and complete the sentences using these words:

   amperes   watts   volts

   Potential difference is measured in _____ .
   Power is measured in _____ .
   Current is measured in _____ .

Static electricity and mains electricity

Static electricity

In solid conductors (e.g. copper wires) the electric current is a flow of electrons.

Many materials are not good conductors – electrons will not flow freely through them. These materials can build up an electrical charge. If you take two materials and rub them together (e.g. a plastic strip and a dry woollen cloth), electrons will pass from one to the other. The material losing electrons becomes positively charged. The material gaining electrons becomes negatively charged. This is **static electricity** and the materials are **electrically charged**.

A charged object can attract small, light objects. So, for example, if you charge up a balloon against your jumper and then hold it against your hair it will often attract your hair.

Two objects with the same charge repel each other. Two objects with opposite charges attract each other.

Uses and dangers of static electricity

One danger of static electricity is using an umbrella in a thunderstorm. The lightning may 'earth' through the metal frame of the umbrella. One use is in electrostatic paint spraying. This ensures a good, even 'finish' when spraying a car.

Mains electricity

Our electricity supply is about 230 V. This can kill if it is not used safely. Most appliances are connected to the mains by a cable and a three-pin plug. Wiring plugs correctly and using the correct fuses are two important parts of electrical safety.

Cables and plugs

The cable has:

- two or three inner wires of copper (a good conductor) to carry the current

- an outer, flexible cover made of plastic (a good insulator) to prevent the current flowing through anyone handling the cable.

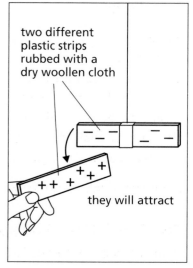

two different plastic strips rubbed with a dry woollen cloth

they will attract

Static electricity

Help

Like charges repel.
Opposite charges attract.

The plug has:

- a plastic or rubber case (a good insulator)
- pins (to fit in the socket) made of brass (a good conductor)
- a fuse
- an earth pin
- a cable grip.

Fuses

The fuse has a current rating. That is, a certain level of current can flow through it. A 13 amp fuse will take a current of 13 amps. If a higher current flows through the fuse, it melts or breaks. This breaks the circuit and stops the current going through the appliance. A current which is too high could damage the appliance and also cause a fire.

Appliances with metal cases are usually earthed.

How to connect the plug

The correct way to do this is:

- blue wire connected to neutral terminal
- brown wire connected through the fuse to the live terminal
- green/yellow wire (if fitted) connected to earth terminal
- cable grip to hold the cable securely in place for safety
- the correct rating of fuse.

You must be able to identify errors in the wiring of a plug.

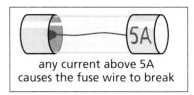

any current above 5A
causes the fuse wire to break

A 5-amp fuse

Help

Appliances have a fuse rating a little higher than their own current rating otherwise the circuit would keep breaking. You should always use the recommended fuse rating.

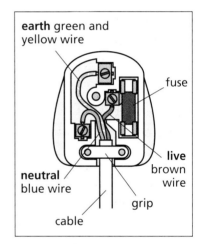

A 3-pin plug

Questions

1 This question is about wiring up a plug. Copy and complete the table using these words:

   blue   brown   green/yellow

	Colour of wire
neutral	
earth	
live	

2 Copy and complete these sentences about static electricity. Use words from this list:

   negatively   rub   positively   charge

   If you _____ two materials together then you may build up a _____. Electrons may pass from one material to another. The material losing electrons will become _____ charged, and the material gaining electrons will become _____ charged.

Electromagnets

Magnets

If a bar magnet is free to move (as in a compass) it will come to rest with one end pointing north and the other pointing south. The end pointing north is called the north-seeking pole, and the other end is the south-seeking pole.

If the north-seeking pole of one magnet is put next to the north-seeking pole of another magnet, they will repel each other. But if it is put next to the south-seeking pole they will attract. Opposite poles attract, and similar poles repel.

A magnet also has a **magnetic field** around it, which has an effect on any nearby magnetic material (e.g. iron or steel, or another magnet).

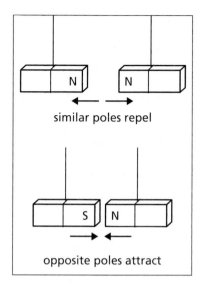
similar poles repel

opposite poles attract

Electromagnets

A coil of wire can behave like a magnet – when it has an electric current running through it. One end of the coil becomes a north pole and the other end a south pole. This is a magnet which can be switched on and off with the electric current. It is called an **electromagnet**.

You can increase the strength of an electromagnet by:

• placing an iron core inside the coil

• increasing the number of turns on the coil

• increasing the size of the current flowing through the coil.

A whole range of electrical appliances and components are based on wires acting like magnets when electric currents flow through them.

If you reverse the current, you reverse the poles of the magnet.

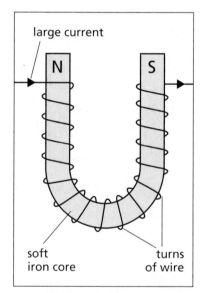
large current

soft iron core   turns of wire

A simple electromagnet

Circuit breakers

Circuit breakers are increasingly used instead of fuses in some appliances. They contain an electromagnet. When the current becomes high enough, then the strength of the electromagnet increases enough to separate a pair of contacts. This breaks the circuit. Circuit breakers work more quickly than fuses and are easy to reset by pressing a button.

The electric motor

If you place a wire carrying a current in a magnetic field, it experiences a force. The size of this force can be increased by:

- increasing the strength of the magnetic field
- increasing the size of the current flowing through the wire.

If the direction of the field or the current is reversed, the wire experiences an opposite force.

This is basically how an electric motor works – a coil of wire turns or spins because of magnetic forces.

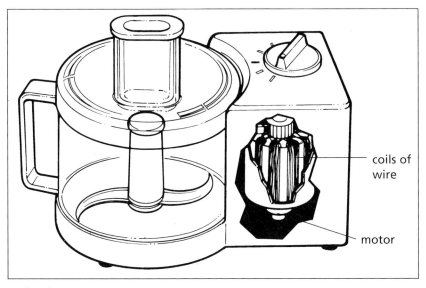

A food processor

Questions

1 Suggest *two* ways in which circuit breakers are better than fuses.

2 Give *two* ways of increasing the force produced by an electric motor.

3 Draw a spider diagram to show *three* different ways the strength of an electromagnet can be increased. Put **increasing strength** at the centre of your diagram.

Using magnets in appliances

The door bell

The electromagnet in this case is used to work a bell push.

This is how it works.

- You press the bell push. The circuit is complete and a current flows.
- The electromagnet works and pulls the soft iron. The hammer hits the gong.
- The contact screw is not now contacting the springy metal strip. The circuit therefore breaks and the electromagnet stops working.
- The hammer springs back. The contact screw is now in contact again with the springy metal strip, so the circuit is complete again and the current flows.
- The bell continues to ring (the hammer keeps hitting the gong) until you take your finger off the bell push and break the circuit.

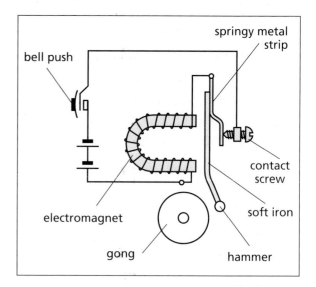

 **Help**

When you press the bell push, the circuit is continually broken and remade. So the hammer doesn't just hit the gong once, but continues to hit it until you release the bell push.

The d.c. motor

The electromagnet is used to turn a coil.

This is how it works.

- The battery is turned on. The current flows.
- The coil turns due to the force fields from the magnets at either side.
- When the coil is vertical the forces are equal but the momentum of the coil carries it over.
- The split ring keeps switching the direction of the current so that it flows first one way and then the other, to keep the coil spinning.

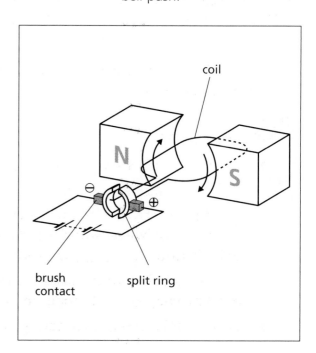

The loudspeaker

The electromagnet is used to create sound waves.

This is how it works.

- As a current flows through the coil it develops a magnetic force.
- The magnet also has a field and the magnet and the coil interact.
- The cone moves (vibrates) in and out.
- These vibrations result in sound waves.

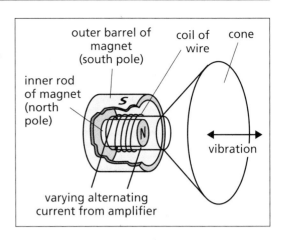

The relay

An electromagnet is used to help a weak current trigger a stronger current.

For example, the starter motor of a car requires 100 A to work. The current is carried in short, expensive, thick wires from the car battery. An electromagnet is used to link the switch on the dashboard, the starter motor and the battery.

This is how it works.

- Long, thin, cheap wires from the dashboard switch carry current which causes the electromagnet to work.
- This attracts the soft iron at the top of the pivot. The movement of the pivot closes the contacts and the circuit to the battery is complete.

One circuit therefore results in another being 'switched on' for a short period.

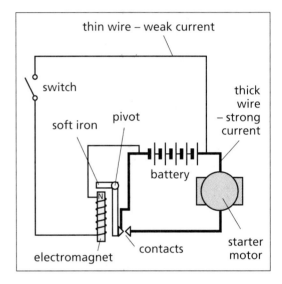

 Questions

1 Copy and complete the sentences using words from this list:

magnets   battery   momentum   current

In a d.c. motor, when you turn the _____ on a _____ flows. The coil turns due to the force fields produced by _____ on either side. When the coil is vertical its _____ carries it over.

2 In a loudspeaker, what causes the sound to be produced?
A electromagnets   **B** cone vibrating   **C** force fields produced.

3 Why is a relay used when starting a car?

Making and supplying electricity

The generator

If you rotate a coil of wire in a magnetic field then you will induce an electric current. This is how the **generator** works.

Other ways of generating electricity would be to rotate the magnets around the coil, or to move a magnet in and out of a coil.

As the coil of wire cuts through the lines of force of the magnetic field, a voltage (potential difference) is produced between the ends of the wire. If the wire is part of a complete circuit then a current will flow. This is how a bicycle dynamo lamp works.

Help

The generator – spinning movement within magnetic field = electrical current.

The motor – electrical current within magnetic field = spinning movement.

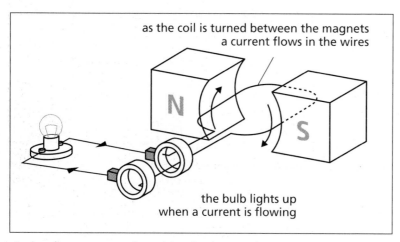

as the coil is turned between the magnets a current flows in the wires

the bulb lights up when a current is flowing

A simple generator (e.g. bicycle dynamo)

You can increase the size of the voltage by doing any, or all, of the following things:

• move the wire faster

• increase the strength of the magnetic field

• increase the number of turns on the coil of wire.

This is the principle behind electricity generating power stations. In most power stations steam is used to drive turbines, which in turn drive the generators. The generators then produce electricity.

Using tidal or hydroelectric power, it is water that drives the turbines. Steam does not need to be produced by burning fossil fuels so these methods are environmentally more 'friendly'.

What is a.c. and d.c. current?

The current produced by generators is **alternating current** (a.c.). This means that it is always changing direction. It changes 50 times a second (known as the **frequency**). This is 50 hertz (Hz).

Cells and batteries supply current flowing in one direction only. This is **direct current** (d.c.).

Transformers

These are used to change the voltage in an a.c. supply. The National Grid brings electricity to your home at perhaps 250 000 volts – not much use for your television! Transformers bring it back down to 230 volts.

As the electricity leaves the power station, transformers increase the voltage to transmit it efficiently through the power lines. Transformers near homes then reduce this voltage so that it can be used with household appliances.

The higher the voltage transmitted in our power lines, the smaller the current needed to transmit electricity at the same rate. A high current would heat up the power lines and so waste energy.

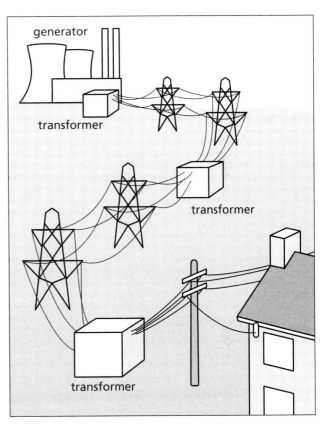

Supplying electricity to your home

 Questions

1   Draw a spider diagram to show *three* different ways of increasing the voltage produced by a generator. Put **increasing voltage** at the centre of your diagram.

2   Copy and complete the sentences using these words:

   potential difference   rotated   magnetic field   lines of force

   To produce electricity a coil of wire is _____ in a _____ . The wire cuts through the _____ . A voltage (_____) is produced between the ends of the wire.

3   Why do we use transformers?

Module test questions

1 The diagram shows some components which may be found as part of an electrical circuit.
Choose words from the list for each of the components **1–4** in the diagram.

resistor
diode
fuse
thermistor

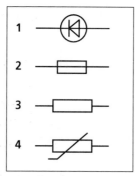

2 This question is about using a plug safely.
Copy and complete the table using words from this list.

fuse
blue wire
brown wire
green/yellow wire

	Inside a plug
1	connected to the earth
2	connected to the neutral
3	protects the circuit
4	connected to the live

3 This question is about how a loudspeaker works.
Sentences **1–4** describe what happens when you use a loudspeaker. Put the sentences into the correct order.

1 the cone vibrates in and out
2 the current flows and the coil develops a magnetic field
3 the vibrations produce sound
4 the field of the coil interacts with the magnets.

4 Match the units in this list with each of numbers **1–4** in the table.
hertz   volt   ampere   watt

	What does the unit represent?
1	power
2	frequency
3	current
4	potential difference

5 Which *two* of these statements are true of the graph showing current against volts?

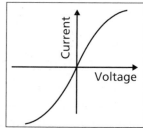

A there is no current if the voltage is reversed
B as the voltage increases so does the current, but eventually the current increases more slowly
C the current is directly proportional to the voltage
D when the voltage is reversed the current still increases as the voltage increases
E the current is inversely proportional to the voltage.

6 This is a diagram of a circuit with two light bulbs set up in parallel.

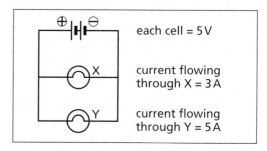

Which *two* of these statements about the circuit are correct?

A the total potential difference produced by the cells is 5 V

B the total current in the circuit is 5 A

C the resistance in the circuit is equal to that of the more resistant bulb

D the total current in the circuit is 8 A

E the total potential difference in the circuit is 10 V.

7   This is a diagram of a bell push circuit. It uses an electromagnet.

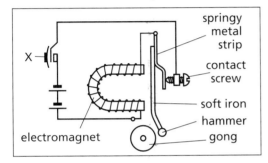

springy metal strip

contact screw

X

soft iron

hammer

gong

electromagnet

1. What happens when you press X?

A the circuit breaks

B the electromagnet stops working

C a current flows

D the soft iron springs back from the electromagnet.

2. What happens as the hammer hits the gong?

A the circuit is completed

B the electromagnet starts to work

C the current stops flowing

D the contact screws start to touch the springy metal strip.

3. What happens when the circuit is broken?

A the current stops flowing

B the hammer hits the gong

C the electromagnet continues to work

D the soft iron is attracted to the electromagnet.

4. How could you increase the strength of the electromagnet?

A decreasing the current

B using thicker wires in the coil

C making the electromagnet thinner

D using more turns of wire for the coil.

8   This is a diagram of a generator.

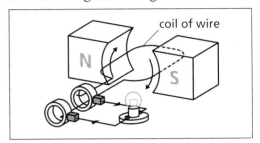

coil of wire

N

S

1. When the coil spins:

A a voltage is induced

B the resistance of the coil increases

C the bulb goes out

D the coil sets up its own magnetic field.

2. Which of the following would not increase the voltage?

A increasing the strength of the magnetic field

B decreasing the area of the coil

C moving the wire faster

D increasing the number of turns on the coil.

3. In which of the following forms of power generation is water *not* turned into steam?

A coal fired   **B** nuclear

C gas fired   **D** hydroelectric.

4. Transformers are used at power stations to:

A decrease the resistance of power lines

B alter the voltage

C allow a greater current to flow

D increase the temperature at which the wires transmit the electricity.

Speed, velocity and acceleration

Speed

If an object moves in a straight line you can show how far it has travelled by a distance–time graph.

You can see in this graph that as time passes the object does not go any further. It is standing still.

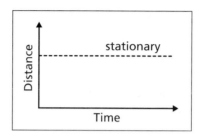

You can see in this graph that as time passes the object is moving further away. The line is straight, which means the object is moving at a steady speed.

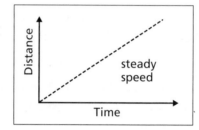

The steeper the slope of the graph, the faster the object is travelling.

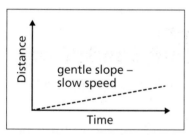
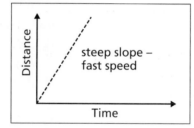

The steeper the slope of the graph, the further the object will travel in the same time.

You can work out an object's speed using this formula:

$$\textbf{speed (m/s)} = \frac{\textbf{distance travelled (m)}}{\textbf{time (s)}}$$

Help

m/s = metres per second
m = metres
s = seconds

Worked example

Q A train travels 100 metres in 5 seconds. What is its speed?

A speed = $\frac{\text{distance}}{\text{time}}$

$= \frac{100}{5} = 20\,\text{m/s}$

Help

Examiners may use km or other units – don't be tricked!

Velocity

Velocity is speed in a straight line.

If you go for a bike ride you will take many left and right turns. You can work out your speed at the end by how far you have ridden in how much time. You would have to ride your bike in a straight line to be able to work out your velocity.

Velocity–time graphs show how an object moves.

Graph **A** shows constant velocity. The object is not getting any faster or slower over time. It is going at the same velocity.

Graph **B** shows that the object is getting faster as time passes. It is **accelerating**. The graph is a straight line, which means the acceleration is constant.

The acceleration of an object is the rate at which its velocity changes. You can work out an object's acceleration using this formula:

$$\textbf{acceleration } (\text{m/s}^2) = \frac{\textbf{change in velocity } (\text{m/s})}{\textbf{time taken for the change } (\text{s})}$$

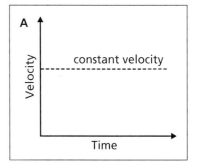

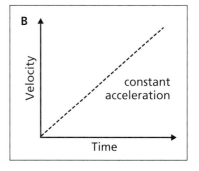

 Worked example

Q A car accelerates from 0 to 30 m/s in 10 seconds. What is the acceleration of the car?

A acceleration $= \dfrac{\text{change in velocity}}{\text{time}}$

$= \dfrac{30}{10} = 3 \, \text{m/s}^2$ (always remember the units)

 *Checkpoint*

Cover the page, then write down the formula for acceleration.
Check your answer.

 Questions

1 A car travels 5000 metres in 200 seconds. What is its speed?

2 An aeroplane accelerates along the runway. In 8 seconds it accelerates from 0 to 56 m/s. What is its acceleration?

3 This graph shows the movement of a car. Study the graph then describe what is happening to the car.

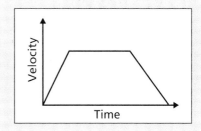

Speeding up and slowing down

Everything is affected by the forces around it. The force from your hand moves the pen and you write. The force of your arm acts on your coffee mug to raise it to your mouth.

Balanced forces

If the forces on an object cancel each other out, there is no change in the object. If it is sitting still, it stays sitting still.

For example, when a boat floats on water:

- the weight of the boat causes a downward force
- the surface of the water exerts an upward force
- if the forces are the same, the boat floats on the water.

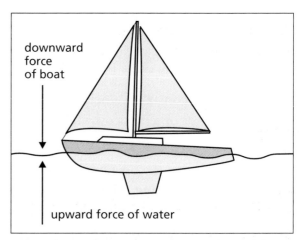

Balanced forces

The forces are **balanced**, so they have no overall effect. If the forces on a moving object are balanced, it carries on at the same speed.

For example:

- if a car is not moving and you don't change the forces acting on it, the car will remain not moving
- if the car is already moving and you don't change the forces acting on it, then the car keeps moving at the same speed.

Help

In these diagrams, the size of the arrows shows the size of the forces.

What happens if you change the forces?

If the forces change, the movement of the object changes.

When a car engine starts, it gives a stationary car greater forward force so the car moves forward.

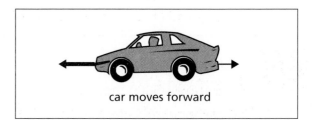
car moves forward

When the car is moving forward, a greater forward force makes it move forward faster.

car moves forward **faster**

When the car is moving forward, a greater opposite force makes it slow down.

car moving forward **now slows down**

When the car is moving forward, the greater the forward force the faster it will go.

Forces that are not equal are said to be **unbalanced**.

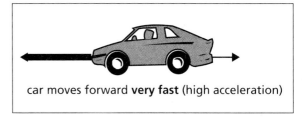

car moves forward **very fast** (high acceleration)

The force of gravity

Objects fall to Earth because of **gravity**. Gravity is a downward force. On Earth the acceleration due to gravity is about 10 N/kg. Your weight is actually your mass in kilograms multiplied by the force of gravity:

weight (N) = **mass** (kg) × **force of gravity** (N/kg)

You do not have to remember this formula, but you must be able to use it.

Help

Weight is often wrongly given in kilograms – bathroom scales show kilograms. This is actually your mass. Your weight is measured in newtons.

Worked example

Q You have a friend whose mass is 45 kg. What is her weight?

A weight = mass × force of gravity

       = 45 × 10

       = 450 N (remember the units)

Checkpoint

Cover the page, then write down the units for:
  weight
  mass
  the force of gravity.
Check your answer.

Questions

1 Why does a boat float on water? Why does it float lower in the water if you add a weight to it?

2 Find out your mass in kilograms. What is your weight in newtons?

3 Describe the size of the forces when:
  a a car is speeding up
  b a car is slowing down.

Friction

Friction is a force. It is there when:

- an object moves through air or water or

- solid surfaces slide over each other.

Friction always acts in the opposite direction to the way the object is moving.

For example:

- if you are swimming, the force of friction slows you down through the water

- when an aeroplane flies through the air, the force of friction (air resistance) is acting to slow it down.

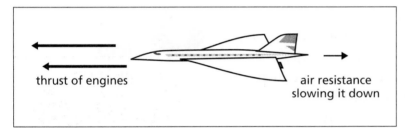

thrust of engines

air resistance slowing it down

 **Checkpoint**

Cover the page, then write down the name of the force which slows down moving things.
Check your answer.

When a car or a plane has a steady speed, the forces of friction are balancing the driving force.

Brakes use friction to slow down a car. The greater the speed of the car:

- the greater the braking force needed to slow down the car in the same time, or

- the longer it takes the car to slow down if you use the same braking force.

If you brake too hard then the car will skid. This is because the tyres lose their grip on the road – there is not enough friction between the tyres and the road.

When a car slows down, the force of friction of the tyres on the road:

- causes the tyres (and the brake pads) to heat up

- wears the tread on the tyres so they need replacing (or they become dangerous and illegal).

The stopping distance of a car depends on:

- the distance the car travels while the driver thinks
- the distance the car travels while the brakes work.

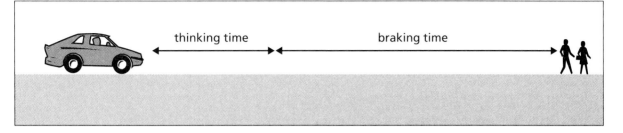

It takes longer to stop a car if:

- the car is travelling faster
- the driver's reactions are slowed down (e.g. tiredness, drink or drugs)
- the road conditions are poor (e.g. it is wet, icy or there is poor visibility)
- the car is not in a roadworthy condition (e.g. worn brakes or tyres).

The faster an object moves through air or water, the greater the force of friction against it.

When a person falls from an aeroplane:

- at first the person speeds up because of gravity
- the force of friction through the air eventually balances the force of gravity
- the forces are now balanced
- the person now falls at a constant speed (stops speeding up).

This is called **terminal velocity.**

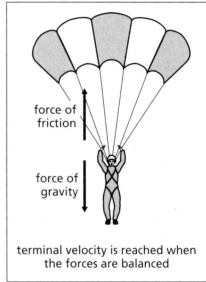

force of friction

force of gravity

terminal velocity is reached when the forces are balanced

Terminal velocity

 Questions

1 Why does a person fall to ground more slowly from an aeroplane when using a parachute?

2 Draw a spider diagram to show the things which would affect how quickly a car stops. Put **car takes longer to stop** at the centre of the diagram.

3 Which *two* forces are balanced when an object falling from the sky reaches terminal velocity?

Transferring energy

Movement

When a force moves an object work is done. If you carry a bag across a room then work has been done.

Work is done by transferring energy from one object to another. You can calculate the work done using this formula:

work done (J) = **force applied** (N) × **distance moved** (m)

Help

J = joule
N = newton
m = metre

 Worked example

Q Chris moves a bag of potatoes weighing 50 N a distance of 20 m. How much work has he done?

A work done = force × distance
         = 50 × 20
         = 1000 J (remember the units)

Energy transferred (work done) against a frictional force usually takes the form of heat.

Help

In physics, 'work done' means that energy has been transferred from one object to another.

Kinetic energy

An object has kinetic energy if it is moving. If a train is moving it has kinetic energy.

An object has more kinetic energy:

• the greater its mass (a larger train)

• the greater its speed (a faster train).

Checkpoint

Cover the page, then write down the formula for work done.
Check your answer.

Elastic energy

If you stretch a spring or a piece of elastic:

- before you let it go it has (elastic) **potential energy** – the ability to do work

- if you let it go it has (elastic) **kinetic energy**.

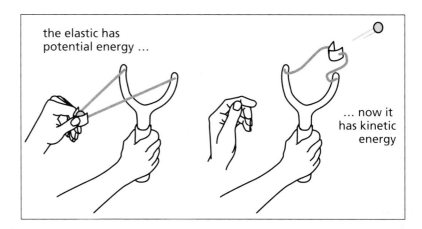

the elastic has potential energy …

… now it has kinetic energy

If you stretch a spring too far, its **elastic limit** is passed and it is deformed permanently (for ever). It will not return to normal.

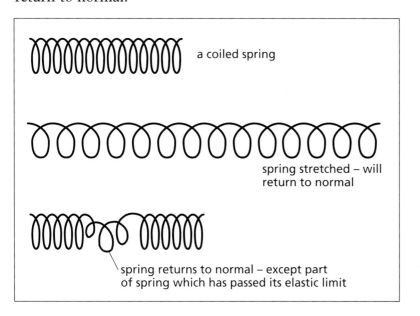

a coiled spring

spring stretched – will return to normal

spring returns to normal – except part of spring which has passed its elastic limit

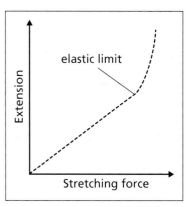

elastic limit

Extension

Stretching force

Questions

1   Joanna carries her school bag to school. It weighs 200 N. Joanna carries the bag 450 m. How much work has she done?

2   A family car is travelling at the same speed as the articulated lorry behind it. Which has the greater kinetic energy, and why?

3   Malcolm decides to do a 'bungee' jump. He jumps off the bridge and dives towards the river. He is able to put his hand in the river just before 'springing' back up again. If the bungee passes its elastic limit on the dive down, what is likely to happen?

Pressure

Try to push a blunt
nail into wood – it is
really difficult.
Try to push a sharp
nail into wood – it is
much easier.

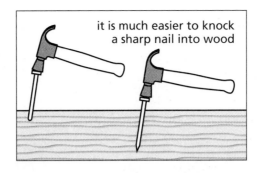

it is much easier to knock
a sharp nail into wood

The greater the force over an area, the greater the pressure:

$$\textbf{pressure (N/m}^2) = \frac{\textbf{force (N)}}{\textbf{area (m}^2)}$$

A pressure of 1 pascal is exerted by a force of 1 newton
acting at right angles to an area of 1 metre squared (m²).

Help

$\textbf{N/m}^2$ = newtons per metre
square

$\textbf{N}$ = newton

$\textbf{m}$ = metre

$\textbf{Pa}$ = equivalent to N/m²

 Worked example

Q A block of wood is on a table. The block exerts a force of 200 N on the
table (it weighs 200 N). It covers an area of 4 m² of the table.
What pressure does it exert?

A pressure = $\dfrac{\text{force}}{\text{area}}$

= $\dfrac{200}{4}$

= 50 N/m²
or 50 pascals
(remember the units)

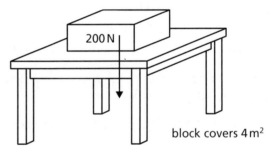

200 N

block covers 4 m²

 Worked example

This example includes a typical examiner's trick!

Q A tractor is standing in a field. It exerts a force
of 10 000 N on the soil. Each of its wheels has
an area of 0.4 m² in contact with the soil.
What pressure does it exert on the soil?
(Remember it has four wheels!)

A pressure = $\dfrac{\text{force}}{\text{area}}$

= $\dfrac{10\,000}{1.6}$
(four wheels each 0.4 m²)

= 6250 N/m²

Checkpoint

Cover the page, then write
down the formula for
pressure.
Check your answer.

Hydraulic systems

If you try lifting a car with your hands, you can't!
You can if you use a hydraulic jack. This means that the
jack is a **force multiplier**. It makes the force you can
exert much bigger. If you press the lever at one end, a
much bigger force is developed at the other end.

Just think!

If it wasn't for car jacks, we could never change a tyre!

Another good example is the car's braking system.

What happens is this:

• you push on the brake pedal
• this applies a force to the
  master piston
• this puts pressure on the brake fluid
• the fluid puts pressure on the car brakes
  – through the **slave piston**
• the car brakes press against the wheel
• the car stops.

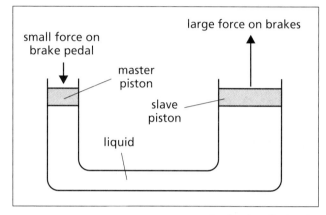

An hydraulic brake

This system makes the force with which you press on the
brake pedal much bigger – otherwise the car wouldn't stop!

There are two other facts that you need to know about
pressure in liquids:

• at any point in the liquid the force acts equally in all
  directions
• pressure in a liquid increases with depth.

Questions

1   A wooden post is hammered into the soil. The force used is 1200 N and the area
    of the post entering the soil is 0.05 m². What pressure is exerted on the soil?

2   Why does the hull of a submarine have to be much stronger than the hull of
    a surface ship?

3   Copy and complete the sentences using words from this list:

    slave   force   smaller   pressure   master   bigger

    When you press the brake of a car you apply a _____ to the _____
    piston. This puts _____ on the brake fluid. This fluid, in turn, acts on
    the _____ piston. The system results in a much _____ force being
    transferred to the car brakes.

Earth in space

Day and night

The Earth turns around once on its axis every 24 hours. The half of the Earth facing the Sun is in daylight, in the other half it is night.

It takes the Earth 365 days to orbit the Sun.

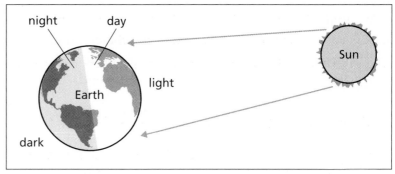

Day and night

The planets

There are other planets in our solar system. We see them because they reflect the Sun's light – they do not give out light of their own.

The orbits of the planets are squashed circles (called **ellipses**). The Sun is quite close to the centre of all of these orbits.

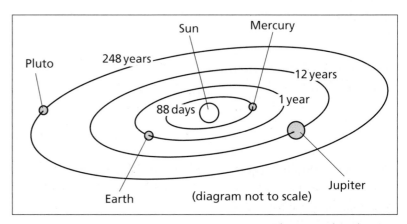

Planets orbit the Sun

All planets attract each other with the force of gravity. The greater the distance between them, the smaller the force of gravity.

A smaller body (e.g the Moon around the Earth) will stay in orbit because of the combination of high speed and the force of gravity. Satellites stay in orbit for the same reason as the planets – a combination of high speed and the force of gravity.

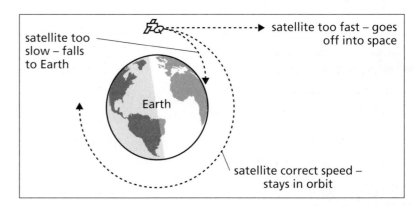

Staying in orbit

The planets appear in different positions at different times of year. It depends where the different planets are in their orbits.

Satellites

Satellites are put into orbit. They are used to:

- send information between places a long way apart
- look at weather conditions across the planet
- look at the Universe without our atmosphere getting in the way.

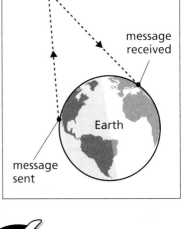

satellite

message received

Earth

message sent

The start of the Universe

Our Sun is only one of many millions of stars in a group called the Milky Way. The Milky Way is a **galaxy**.

The stars in the Milky Way are millions of times further away than the planets in our solar system – a very long way off!

The Universe is made up of billions of galaxies just like our Milky Way, and galaxies are often many millions of times further apart than stars in a galaxy.

The Universe is really so big it is impossible to imagine it.

We think that the stars were formed from dust and gas. There was so much of it that it was pulled together by **gravitational attraction.**

We think that small masses formed as well. These became planets orbiting around the larger masses (the stars).

Our solar system

People once thought that the Earth was the centre of our solar system. However, by careful observation of the movement of the planets it became obvious that the Sun was at the centre of our solar system. The planets, including the Earth, orbit the Sun.

The stars you can see at night stay in fixed patterns – these are called **constellations**.

 *Checkpoint*

Cover the page, then write down *three* uses of satellites. Check your answer.

 **Just think!**

Some stars are so far away that if they blew up now we wouldn't know for millions of years.

 Questions

1   The Hubble telescope orbits the Earth. How is it able to do this?

2   The Hubble telescope is able to take much clearer pictures of space than we can take from Earth. Suggest a reason for this.

3   Planets do not produce any light of their own. How are we able to see them?

Terminal exam questions

1 Here is a car.

a When the car is loaded the area of each tyre in contact with the ground is 13 cm by 15 cm.

i Calculate the area of *one* tyre in contact with the ground. [2]

ii The car has four tyres. Calculate the total area in contact with the ground. [1]

b When the vehicle is loaded it weighs 15 600 N.
Calculate the pressure exerted on the ground by the tyres. [3]

[6 marks]

2 a Samantha has a mass of 50 kg. Use the information below to work out her weight. [2]

weight = mass × gravitational field strength

gravitational field strength on Earth is 10 N/kg

b Samantha's bag weighs 120 N. She moves her bag over a distance of 15 m. How much work has she done? [3]

c State *two* ways that you can increase the kinetic energy of an object. [2]

[7 marks]

3 a You travel into town on your bike. You cycle 1200 metres and take 200 seconds to complete the journey. What is your average speed? [3]

b You start off at rest. After 10 seconds your speed is 5 m/s. What is your acceleration? [3]

c Name *one* force which is stopping you accelerating any faster. [1]

[7 marks]

4 a Give *three* uses of satellites. [3]

b How do satellites manage to stay in orbit? [2]

[5 marks]

5 This is a distance–time graph of a car journey.

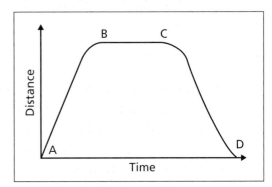

a Between which two points is the car travelling away from the starting point? [2]

b Between which two points is the car stationary (not moving)? [2]

c At which point has the car returned to where it started? [1]

[5 marks]

Total for test: 30 marks

Making waves

It is easy to make waves in ropes, swings and across the surface of water (e.g. ripples on the surface of a pond).

What are waves?

A wave is a regular pattern of disturbances. It moves energy from one place to another without taking any substance with it. So, for example, a wave travelling through a metal spring does not carry metal from the beginning to the end of the spring.

The 'height' of a wave is called its **amplitude**. The distance between one point on a wave and the same point on the next is called the **wavelength**. The number of waves passing a point per second is the **frequency**. This is measured in hertz (Hz) which is the number of waves per second. For example, 50 Hz is 50 waves per second.

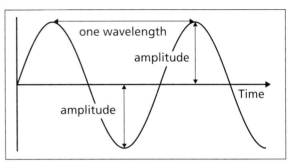

Measuring a wave

Pitch

If a wave makes an object vibrate it makes a sound. The greater the frequency of the vibrations, the higher the **pitch** of the sound. A low voice has a low frequency. A high voice has a high frequency.

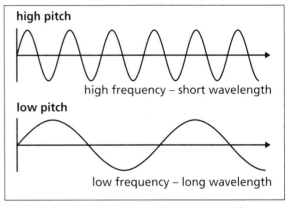

Measuring pitch

Question

1 Look at the four diagrams of sound waves. Which shows the wave with:
   a the highest frequency
   b the longest wavelength
   c the greatest amplitude?

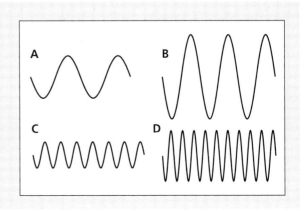

More about waves

The oscilloscope

This piece of equipment is very useful for showing vibrations as waves. For example a tuning fork makes vibrations. We hear the vibrations as sound. The oscilloscope shows the vibrations as a wave.

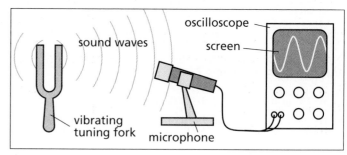

Sound waves show up on an oscilloscope

Ultrasound

Electronic systems can be used to produce **ultrasonic waves**. They are called ultrasonic because we cannot hear them. They are too high pitched.

These ultrasonic waves can be used:

• in industry for cleaning and quality control

• to check on a baby's development in the womb.

Reflection

Light and sound are waves. Sounds bounce back from hard surfaces. These are called echoes. If you shout at a cliff face then your voice echoes (it has bounced back to you from the cliff face).

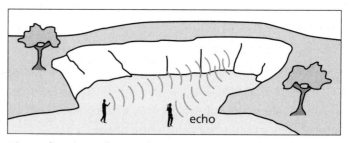

The reflection of sound

When a light ray hits a shiny surface like a mirror it **reflects** from it. If a light ray hits a flat, shiny surface at an angle, it leaves the surface (is reflected) at the same angle.

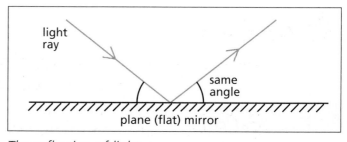

The reflection of light

Internal reflection

When a ray of light travels from glass, perspex or water into air then some of the light is also reflected at the boundary.

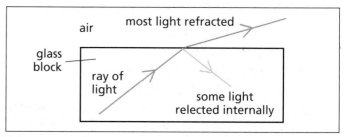

Internal reflection

Refraction

When a ray of light passes from one transparent substance to another e.g. from air into glass it changes direction. This is called **refraction**. The light changes direction as it crosses the **boundary** from one substance into another.

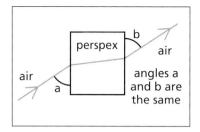

If light passes into another substance along the **normal** (that is at right angles to it) then the light continues in a straight line. In other words, the light does not refract.

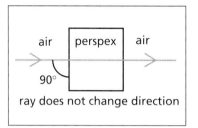

If you pass white light through a prism the light splits into different colours, because each colour is refracted to a different extent. This results in a spectrum which has the same colours in the same order as a rainbow.

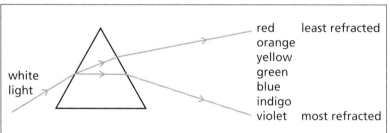

Help

Richard Of York Gained Battles In Vain – this will help you to remember the colours in the correct order!

Water waves can also be refracted when they cross the boundary between two different substances.

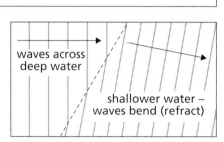

Refraction of water waves

 Questions

1 Copy and complete the sentences using these two words:

   reflected   refracted

   When a ray of light hits a plane mirror the light is _____. If it travels from water into air most of the light is _____ but some is _____ at the boundary. When a wave on the sea slows down as it reaches the shore it is _____.

2 Look at these diagrams then answer the questions.
   a Draw diagrams of how light rays 1 and 2 will reflect.
   b Draw diagrams of how light rays 3 and 4 will refract.

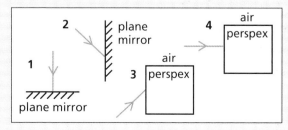

Electromagnetic radiation

Light is only one form of **electromagnetic radiation**. But what *is* electromagnetic radiation? The answer is – waves that can pass through space (that is, through a vacuum).

There is a continuous spectrum of electromagnetic radiation. We cannot see most of it. Different types of electromagnetic radiation have different frequencies and wavelengths.

These different forms of electromagnetic radiation are all absorbed or transmitted in different ways by:

- different substances and
- different types of surface.

On these two pages you will find examples of the uses of different types of radiation.

When radiation is absorbed the energy it carries:

- makes the substance hotter
- may create an alternating electric current with the same frequency as the radiation itself (this is how a television works).

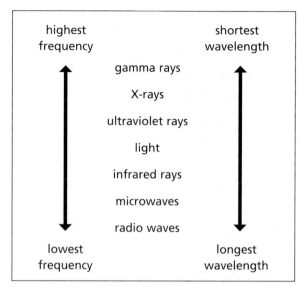

The spectrum of electromagnetic radiation

 **Checkpoint**

Cover the page, then write down *three* types of electromagnetic radiation. Check your answer.

Using electromagnetic radiation

The effects and uses of the different types of radiation depend on their various properties.

Radio waves

These are used to transmit radio and TV programmes all over the Earth. The longer wavelength radio waves are reflected back to Earth from an electrically charged layer in the Earth's upper atmosphere. This means that the waves can be sent around the Earth, even though it is a sphere.

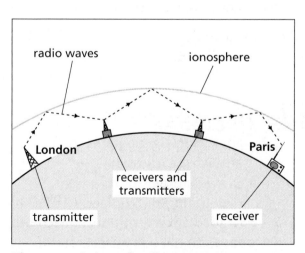

The transmission of radio waves

Microwaves

These can easily pass through the Earth's atmosphere. They are therefore used to pass information to and receive information from satellites. Microwave radiation (with wavelengths strongly absorbed by water particles) is used in microwave cookers for cooking food or heating drinks.

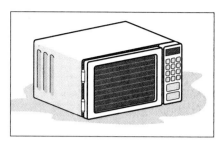

A microwave oven

Infrared radiation

This is used in grills, toasters and radiant heaters (like electric fires). It is also used to carry telephone messages along optical fibres and for TV and remote video controls.

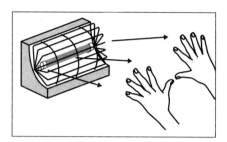

An electric fire

Visible light

Doctors use endoscopes to look inside people. Endoscopes work by sending light down optical fibres (fine glass tubes). The light stays inside the fibres and doesn't come out until it reaches the end. The light stays in the fibre because it is reflected from side to side and so is 'bounced' all the way down to the end.

This is called **total internal reflection**. It happens when the light hits the inside of the fibre at an angle greater than an angle which is called the 'critical angle'.

In an endoscope, some bundles of fibres carry the light down into the patient's body. Other bundles carry the light reflected from inside the body back up into the doctor's eye. These are called **optical fibres**.

Optical fibres are now also used for carrying cable TV and some telephone calls. The fibres can also be used to carry light to illuminate car dashboards.

They can carry more information than electrical signals down a cable of the same size.

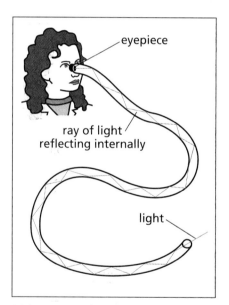

Using an endoscope

Questions

1 Arrange these *four* types of radiation in order. Put the type with longest wavelength first, and the type with the shortest wavelength last.

   ultraviolet rays   microwaves   gamma rays   X-rays

2 Astronauts cannot shout at each other through space on a space walk. Why does this tell you that sound is not a type of electromagnetic radiation?

More electromagnetic radiation

More uses

Ultraviolet radiation

This is used to make white people go 'brown' on sun beds. Special coatings which absorb UV radiation and emit it well are used both in fluorescent lamps and for security coding.

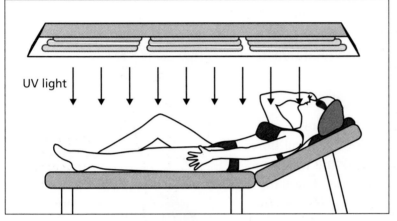

UV light

Sun-beds use UV light

Just think!

When white people lie on the beach to sunbathe, it is UV radiation that makes them go brown.

X radiation

X radiation (X-rays) does not pass easily through some materials (e.g. bone). It is used to make shadow pictures. Pictures can be made of broken bones or cracks inside metal structures (e.g. bridges).

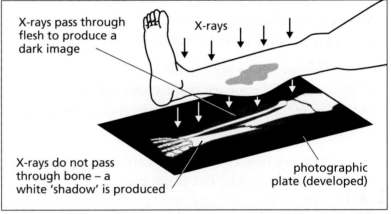

X-rays pass through flesh to produce a dark image

X-rays

X-rays do not pass through bone – a white 'shadow' is produced

photographic plate (developed)

X-rays are used to photograph broken bone

Gamma radiation

This is used to:

- kill harmful bacteria in food
- sterilise surgical instruments
- kill cancer cells.

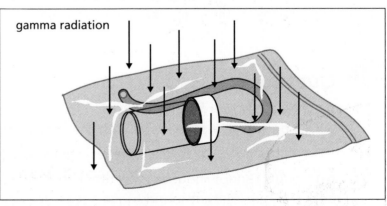

gamma radiation

Gamma radiation is used for sterilising medical equipment

Dangers of radiation

Some radiation can be harmful:

- **Microwaves** are absorbed by the water in living cells. This heats up and the cells can be killed or damaged.

- **Infrared radiation** is absorbed by the skin and felt as heat.

- **Ultraviolet radiation** can pass through the surface of the skin to deeper tissues. The darker the skin, the more it absorbs UV radiation and protects the body. This is why, in general, people living near the equator have dark skin (it is very sunny and hot) and people living near the north pole are very pale (it is not very sunny and certainly not hot!)

- **X-rays and gamma rays** mostly go straight through the skin and soft tissues, but some is absorbed by the cells.

- High doses of UV, X-rays and gamma rays can kill normal cells. Lower doses can cause normal body cells to become cancer cells.

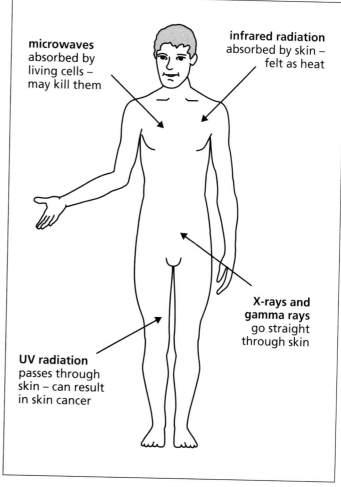

microwaves absorbed by living cells – may kill them

infrared radiation absorbed by skin – felt as heat

X-rays and gamma rays go straight through skin

UV radiation passes through skin – can result in skin cancer

Help

Gamma radiation can both cause and get rid of cancer.

Questions

1 Copy and complete the table using these words:

X-rays
infrared
radio waves
ultraviolet

Type of radiation	Use
	TV remote controls
	transmit information
	sun-beds
	take pictures of fractures

2 Why are X-rays used to show broken bones?

3 Name *one* type of useful electromagnetic radiation. Describe its use and how it might be harmful.

Radioactive substances

There are substances that give out radiation all of the time. They are all around us in the air, building materials and food. Radiation also reaches us from space. This is all called **background radiation**.

There are various sorts of radiation, including:

- **alpha** (α) radiation – easily absorbed by a few centimetres of air or a thin sheet of paper

- **beta** (β) radiation – passes through paper but is absorbed by a few centimetres of metal

- **gamma** (γ) radiation – very penetrating, it needs a few centimetres of lead or several metres of concrete to stop the rays.

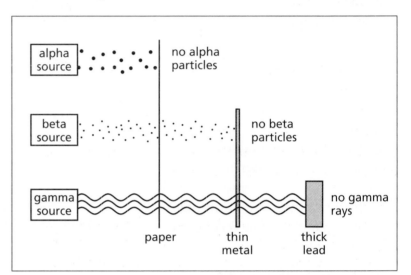

What does radiation do?

Causing and killing cancer
If radiation bumps into neutral atoms or molecules these may become charged ions.

When radiation ionises molecules in living cells it can cause damage, including cancer. The bigger the dose of radiation you have, the higher the chances of getting cancer.

Very high doses of radiation can kill cells. They are used to kill cancer cells and harmful microbes such as bacteria.

Testing thickness
As radiation is absorbed by different thicknesses of various substances it can be used to test them in industry. For example, alpha radiation is used to test the thickness of paper as it is manufactured.

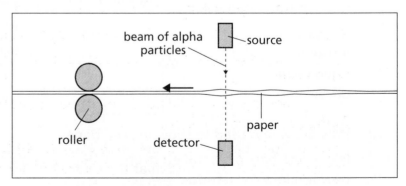

Testing the thickness of paper

The structure of the atom

Alpha and beta radiation is caused by changes in the nucleus of an atom.

Atoms have a small nucleus made up from **protons** and **neutrons**. **Electrons** move around the nucleus.

The mass and charge for each are shown in the table.

	Mass	Charge
proton	1	+1
neutron	1	0
electron	hardly anything	−1

There are always the same number of protons and electrons in an atom. This means that an atom as a whole has no electrical charge. The number of protons and neutrons together is known as the **mass number.**

All the atoms in an element have the same number of protons – the **proton number** (e.g. sodium always has 11 protons). But the number of neutrons in the atoms of an element might vary. Atoms of an element with different numbers of neutrons are known as **isotopes**.

Checkpoint

Cover the page, then write down what an isotope is. Check your answer.

Questions

1 Why is gamma radiation not used in testing the thickness of paper?

2 Copy and complete the sentences using these words:

   alpha   background   gamma   beta

   _____ radiation will pass through a metre of concrete.

   _____ radiation is stopped by a thin sheet of paper.

   _____ radiation passes through paper but is stopped by a few centimetres of metal.

   _____ radiation is the radiation which reaches us from space as well as from some natural minerals.

3 Draw a spider diagram to show *three* ways in which we use radiation usefully. Put **uses of radiation** at the centre of your diagram.

Discovering the atom

An early idea of the atom was the 'plum pudding model'. Scientists described the atom as like a positively charged sphere with negative electrons studded throughout it, like raisins in a pudding.

In 1911 Ernest Rutherford carried out an experiment in which he fired alpha particles at a very thin piece of gold foil. Most went straight through, and only a few were scattered at wide angles by the foil. This was a surprise because, as in the plum pudding model, he expected the particles to bounce off the positively charged spheres of the atoms.

Rutherford concluded that most of an atom was empty space, with a tiny nucleus. If an atom was the size of a school hall its nucleus would be the size of a full stop! This work led to our present idea of the atom.

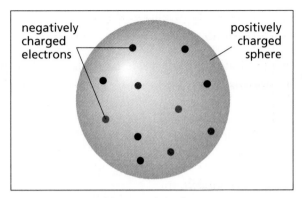

The 'plum pudding' model of an atom

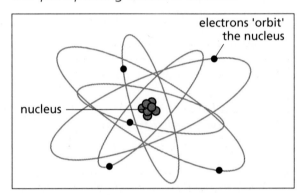

The structure of an atom

Radioactive isotopes

These have unstable nuclei which break down quite readily. When the nucleus breaks down (disintegrates):

- it gives out (emits) radiation
- a different atom is left with a different number of protons.

This is how alpha and beta radiation are produced.

The older the radioactive material, the less radiation it emits. We use this idea to find out how old things are (e.g. rocks).

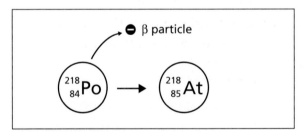

Radioactive polonium becomes astatine as it breaks down

Terminal exam questions

1 Copy this diagram of a wave.

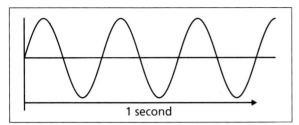

1 second

a i Mark on the diagram *one* wavelength. [1]

ii What is the frequency of the wave? [1]

b These diagrams show two different sound waves, A and B.

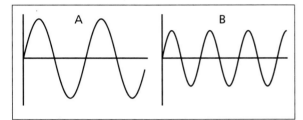

i Which of the waves shows the loudest sound? Explain your answer. [2]

ii Which sound has the highest pitch? Explain your answer. [2]

c i Copy and complete the diagram of a light ray passing through a glass block. [3]

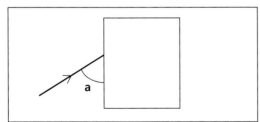

ii What is meant by 'refraction'? [1]

iii What causes the refraction of a wave? [1]

[11 marks]

2 a Copy and complete the diagram to show how white light is split up by a prism. (You need to show only red and blue light) [3]

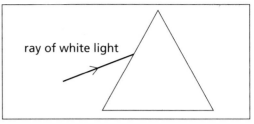

ray of white light

b Visible light is one form of electromagnetic radiation. What is electromagnetic radiation? [2]

c Copy and complete the spectrum of electromagnetic radiation. Use words from this list to match the spaces 1–4. [4]

**X-rays   infrared
visible light   radio waves**

highest frequency ↑ gamma rays
_____1_____
ultraviolet
_____2_____
_____3_____
microwaves
lowest frequency ↓ _____4_____

d Match the type of radiation with its uses as shown in the table. Use words from the list. [4]

**X-rays   microwaves
infrared   ultraviolet**

	Use
1	used to make toast (e.g. in a toaster)
2	used to transmit to satellites
3	used with sunbeds
4	used to photograph broken bones

e What is meant by 'total internal reflection'? [1]

[14 marks]

Total for test: 25 marks

Answers to module tests and terminal exam questions

Humans as Organisms

Question	Answer	Marks	Total
1	1 reproduce 2 respire 3 excrete 4 respond	1 1 1 1	 4
2	1 red cells 2 plasma 3 platelets 4 white cells	1 1 1 1	 4
3	1 trachea 2 bronchus 3 air sac 4 rib	1 1 1 1	 4

Question	Answer	Marks	Total
4	1 fat 2 protein 3 carbohydrate 4 protein	1 1 1 1	 4
5	C and E	2	2
6	A and D	2	2
7	1. B 2. C 3. D 4. A	1 1 1 1	 4
8	1. B 2. A 3. D 4. B	1 1 1 1	 4

Total for test: 28 marks

Maintenance of Life

Question	Answer	Marks	Total
1	1 chloroplast 2 nucleus 3 cell wall 4 cytoplasm	1 1 1 1	 4
2	1 stomata 2 guard cells 3 xylem 4 phloem	1 1 1 1	 4
3	1 nose 2 ear 3 tongue 4 skin	1 1 1 1	 4

Question	Answer	Marks	Total
4	1 cell wall 2 nucleus 3 cytoplasm 4 cell membrane	1 1 1 1	 4
5	B and D	2	2
6	B and E	2	2
7	1. A 2. C 3. D 4. B	1 1 1 1	 4
8	1. B 2. C 3. A 4. D	1 1 1 1	 4

Total for test: 28 marks

Environment

Question			Answer	Marks	Total
1	a	i	*Any two from:* • temperature • amount of light/sun • amount of water • availability of carbon dioxide/oxygen.	2	
		ii	*Any two from:* • amount of food/bushes to eat • number of voles to eat them • number of small birds to eat them *or two of the first list if not used in part **i** (excluding amount of sunlight).*	2	
	b	i	It will decrease as not enough caterpillars to eat.	2	
		ii	The population is likely to decrease as the owls will be forced to eat more voles.	2	**8 marks**
2	a	i	Carbon dioxide.	1	
		ii	*Any two from:* • in sugars • in starch • in proteins • in fats.	2	
	b		*Any two from:* • by the plant through respiration or • eaten by animal then through respiration or • eaten by animal which dies decomposes/bacteria break it down through respiration.	4	
	c		Sewage works compost heaps.	1 1	**9 marks**
3	a	i	*Any two from:* • increasing cars/burning of fossil fuels • increasing number of people • increasing industry/need for electricity/power stations.	2	
		ii	*Any two from:* • increased building • dumping waste • quarrying • farming.	2	
	b		*Any three from:* • sewage in water • fertiliser in water • chemicals in water • smoke in air • sulphur dioxide in air • carbon dioxide in air *cont.*		

Question	Answer	Marks	Total
3b *cont.*	• pesticides on land • herbicides (weedkillers) on land. *There are many answers – these are from the syllabus. You will get marks for all correct answers, whether on the syllabus or not. This is the same for all questions where you may write down correct answers not on the syllabus, so long as they are good science.*	3	**7 marks**
4 a i	Water plants.	1	
ii	Pike.	1	
iii	*Either* water beetles *or* tadpoles.	1	
b	Any two from: • space • food • hiding places.	2	
c	It shows the amount of mass available in the food chain or, better still, the amount of energy at each level.	1	**6 marks**

Total for test: 30 marks

Inheritance and Selection

Question	Answer	Marks	Total
1 a	**1** nucleus **2** chromosomes **3** genes **4** alleles	4	
b i	To produce new plants.	1	
ii	Environmental reasons (e.g. nutrients, water or light).	1	
iii	*Any two from:* • warmth • water • nutrients • light.	2	**8 marks**
2 a i	Cell membranes.	1	
ii	Only if both parents are carriers or have the disorder.	1 1	
b i	Affects the nervous system.	1	
ii	In chromosomes/genes only one parent needs to carry the disorder.	1 1	**6 marks**
3 a	*Any three from:* • lack of food • predation • change in climate (e.g. temperature) • disease	3	

Question	Answer	Marks	Total
b	Causes production of abnormal/dead sex cells.	1 1	
	Plus any two from: • causes some cells to multiply • out of control • causes cancer.	2	**7 marks**
4 a i	*Any two from:* • select male and female • with good characteristics • reproduce from them.	2	
ii	Produce young with wanted characteristics.	1 1	
b i	Stop eggs being released.	1 1	
ii	Stimulate/encourage egg production.	1 1	**8 marks**
5 a	Asexual.	1	
b	Produced by cell division for growth (mitosis) they have exactly the same genes as the parent.	1 1	
c	Take male sex cells from a plant which has bigger strawberries and use them to fertilise female sex cells from another plant with large strawberries. Grow the seed you produce. This is known as selective breeding.	2	**5 marks**

Total for test: 34 marks

Metals

Question	Answer	Marks	Total
1	1 strong acid 2 weak acid 3 neutral 4 weak alkali	1 1 1 1	4
2	1 neutralisation 2 reduction 3 oxidation 4 displacement	1 1 1 1	4
3	1 metal chloride 2 metal oxide 3 hydrogen 4 metal hydroxide or oxide	1 1 1 1	4
4	1 strong 2 good conductor of electricity	1 1	

Question	Answer	Marks	Total
	3 easily shaped 4 strong with low density	1 1	4
5	**A** and **E**	2	2
6	**B** and **E**	2	2
7	1. **A** 2. **C** 3. **B** 4. **C**	1 1 1 1	4
8	1. **A** 2. **C** 3. **B** 4. **A**	1 1 1 1	4

Total for test: 28 marks

Earth Materials

Question	Answer	Marks	Total
1	1 sedimentary	1	
	2 metamorphic	1	
	3 magma	1	
	4 igneous	1	4
2	1 concrete	1	
	2 calcium carbonate	1	
	3 quicklime	1	
	4 slaked lime	1	4
3	1 bitumen	1	
	2 gasoline	1	
	3 kerosene	1	
	4 fuel oil	1	4

Question	Answer		Marks	Total
4	1 oxygen		1	
	2 carbon dioxide		1	
	3 sulphur dioxide		1	
	4 nitrogen		1	4
5	**B** and **C**		2	2
6	**A** and **E**		2	2
7	1.	**A**	1	
	2.	**B**	1	
	3.	**D**	1	
	4.	**B**	1	4
8	1.	**C**	1	
	2.	**D**	1	
	3.	**D**	1	
	4.	**D**	1	4

Total for test: 28 marks

Patterns of Chemical Change

Question	Answer	Marks	Total
1	**A** filter funnel	1	
	used to separate solids from liquids	1	
	B Bunsen burner	1	
	used to heat chemicals	1	
	C tripod	1	
	used to stand a beaker on to heat the chemicals inside	1	
	D measuring cylinder	1	
	used to measure (quantify) the volume of a liquid.	1	**8 marks**
2 a	*Any three methods for 3 marks each:*		
	• heat –		
	particles move faster		
	bump into each other more often/bump into each other with more energy		
	• more concentrated –		
	bump into each other more often		
	particles closer together		
	• greater surface area –		
	more particles		
	bump into each other more often		
	• increase the pressure –		
	particles bump into each other more often		
	and with greater energy, only in a gas.		
	• catalyst –		
	lowers the activation energy	max 9	
b	The least amount of energy necessary	1	
	for a reaction to work.	1	**11 marks**

Question	Answer	Marks	Total
3 a i	1 Nitrogen or hydrogen 2 hydrogen or nitrogen 3 oxygen 4 nitric acid.	4	
ii	450° C 200 atmospheres	2	
iii	Iron.	1	
b	It may run off the land into rivers/lakes/ponds when it rains and get into drinking water.	1 1 1 1	
c	A reaction that takes in energy/heat.	1 1	**13 marks**
4 a i	CH_3COOH: $2 \times C = 24$ *for 1 mark* $4 \times H = 4$ *for 1 mark* $2 \times O = 32$ *for 1 mark* $\overline{60}$ *for 1 mark*	4	
ii	$Ca(OH)_2$: $1 \times Ca = 40$ *for 1 mark* $2 \times O = 32$ *for 1 mark* $2 \times H = 2$ *for 1 mark* $\overline{74}$ *for 1 mark*	4	
b i	Water is H_2O M_r is: $O = 16$ $2 \times H = 2$ $\overline{18}$ *for 1 mark* $\%O = \dfrac{16}{18} \times 100$ *for 1 mark* $= 88.9\%$ *for 1 mark*	3	
ii	Calcium carbonate is $CaCO_3$ M_r is: $Ca = 40$ $C = 12$ $3 \times O = 48$ $\overline{100}$ *for 1 mark* $\%C = \dfrac{12}{100} \times 100$ *for 1 mark* $= 12\%$ *for 1 mark*	3	**14 marks**

Total for test: 46 marks

Structures and Bonding

Question			Answer	Marks	Total
1	a	i	Liquid – loosely packed but only small spaces between particles	1	
			gas – very loosely packed with large gaps between particles.	1	
		ii	They move further apart	1	
			they are able to move more freely	1	
			they can slide over each other.	1	
		iii	The particles have more energy	1	
			so more can escape from the liquid.	1	
	b		*Either:*		
			particles move in all directions (randomly)	1	
			they spread out	1	
			eventually filling a space evenly.	1	
			or		
			particles moving	1	
			from an area of high concentration	1	
			to one of low concentration	1	**10 marks**
2	a	i	11	1	
		ii	11	1	
		iii	12	1	
		iv	23	1	
	b		2 electrons in inner shell		
			8 electrons in next shell		
			1 electron in the outer shell (*1 mark off for each mistake*)	2	
	c	i	Fluorine completed as 2, 7		
			one electron moves from potassium		
			the electron moves to fluorine.	3	
		ii	Ionic.	1	**10 marks**
3	a	i	Second column shaded.	1	
		ii	*Any two from:*		
			• hydrogen		
			• lithium		
			• sodium		
			• potassium.	2	
		iii	Fluorine	1	
			chlorine.	1	
	b		There are 8 electrons in the full outer shell	1	
			so it is very difficult to lose or gain electrons.	1	**7 marks**

Total for test: 27 marks

Energy

Question	Answer	Marks	Total
1	1 convection 2 insulation 3 conduction 4 radiation	1 1 1 1	4
2	1 W 2 J 3 s 4 kWh	1 1 1 1	4
3	1 food mixer 2 radio 3 toaster 4 torch	1 1 1 1	4
4	1 uranium 2 coal	1 1	

Question	Answer	Marks	Total
	3 hydroelectric 4 solar	1 1	4
5	C and D	2	2
6	B and E	2	2
7	1. B 2. D 3. B 4. A	1 1 1 1	4
8	1. C 2. B 3. B 4. C	1 1 1 1	4

Total for test: 28 marks

Electricity

Question	Answer	Marks	Total
1	1 diode 2 fuse 3 resistor 4 thermistor	1 1 1 1	4
2	1 green/yellow wire 2 blue wire 3 fuse 4 brown wire	1 1 1 1	4
3	sentence order is **2 4 1 3**	4	4
4	1 watt 2 hertz	1 1	

Question	Answer	Marks	Total
	3 ampere 4 volt	1 1	4
5	B and D	2	2
6	D and E	2	2
7	1. C 2. C 3. A 4. D	1 1 1 1	4
8	1. A 2. B 3. D 4. B	1 1 1 1	4

Total for test: 28 marks

Forces

Question			Answer	Marks	Total
1	a	i	$13 \times 15 =$ 195 cm^2	1 1	
		ii	$4 \times 195 =$ 780 (cm^2)	1	

Question		Answer	Marks	Total
	b	pressure $= \dfrac{force}{area}$ $= \dfrac{15\,600}{780}$ $= 20$ $\quad$ N/cm^2	1 1 1	6 marks
2	a	$50 \times 10 =$ 500 N	1 1	
	b	work = force $\times$ distance $\quad = 120 \times 15$ $\quad = 1800$ $\quad\quad$ J	1 1 1	
	c	Increase mass increase speed	1 1	7 marks
3	a	speed $\quad = \dfrac{distance}{time}$ $\quad\quad = \dfrac{1200}{200}$ $\quad\quad = 6$ $\quad\quad\quad$ m/s	1 1 1	
	b	acceleration $= \dfrac{change\ in\ speed}{time}$ $\quad\quad = \dfrac{5}{10}$ $\quad\quad = 0.5$ $\quad\quad\quad$ m/s^2	1 1 1	
	c	friction *(or suitable explanation)*	1	7 marks
4	a	Observe the Universe observe weather conditions send information across the planet. *Note: there are other answers which are correct* *(e.g. observe other countries).*	1 1 1	
	b	A combination of high speed and the force of gravity.	1 1	5 marks
5	a	A and B	2	
	b	B and C	2	
	c	D	1	5 marks

Total for test: 30 marks

Waves and Radiation

Question	Answer	Marks	Total
1 a i	From one peak to another	1	
ii	3 (hertz or cycles per second) – this means 3 complete waves pass each second	1	
b i	A (no mark unless reason given)	1	
	because the wave has the biggest amplitude (the peaks are bigger)	1	
ii	B (no mark unless reason given)	1	
	because the frequency is higher (waves closer together)	1	
c i	*Plus 1 extra mark for showing angles a and b are the same.*	3	
ii	Changing direction or 'bending'	1	
iii	Changes speed *or* movement from one type of substance to another *or* for water – the sea becomes shallower or deeper.	1	**11 marks**
2 a		3	
b	*Any two from:* • waves • that transfer energy • can pass through space • do not transfer material.	2	
c	1 X-rays 2 visible light 3 infrared 4 radio waves	4	
d	1 infrared 2 microwaves 3 ultraviolet 4 X-rays	4	
e	Light reflected back within the material.	1	**14 marks**

Total for test: 25 marks

Answers to end of spread questions

These notes accompany the questions which are to be found at the end of each double-page spread. They are not mark schemes as these questions are not the same as those you will find in your final examination.

Humans as Organisms

Page 3

1   Those happening at the moment: movement, respiration, sensitivity, growth.
    Those not happening: excretion (except through lungs and skin), reproduction and nutrition (unless you are eating).

2

Type of food	Used for	Found in
protein		
carbohydrate		cereals, fruit, root vegetables
	energy	

3   Cell membrane, nucleus and cytoplasm.

Page 5

1   Salivary glands – carbohydrase; stomach – protease; pancreas – carbohydrase, protease and lipase; small intestine – carbohydrase, protease and lipase.

2
fat in butter
↓
lipase produced in pancreas and small intestine
↓
fatty acids and glycerol in blood

protein in cheese
↓
protease produced in stomach, small intestine and pancreas
↓
amino acids in blood

3   The large intestine is where most of the water in the gut is reabsorbed.

Page 7

1   Oxygen, respire, energy, carbon dioxide, water.

2   The ribs.

3   Increase fitness or ideas about increasing the amount of oxygen exchanged with each breath.

Page 9

1

Parts of the blood	What they do	Structure
	carries many substances	
	carry oxygen	
	helps fight disease	cell with a nucleus
platelets		bits of cells, no nucleus

Page 11

1   The spider diagram should include: a complete skin, scabs forming when the skin is cut, our air passages have the surface covered in mucus, white cells to digest bacteria, white cells to produce antibodies, white cells to produce antitoxins.

2   They have a cell wall and no nucleus.

3   The disease organism could be in the droplets sneezed, someone may breathe these droplets in.

Maintenance of Life

Page 15

1   Cell wall – keeps the cell in shape; chloroplast – containing chlorophyll for photosynthesis; vacuole – containing the cell sap.

2   Carbon dioxide, water, chlorophyll, glucose, oxygen.

3   The grass stops growing as it is so cold (the enzymes work only very slowly when it is cold).

Page 17

1   Xylem, water, nutrients, sugars, phloem.

2   A thick, waxy layer on the surface of the leaf; stomata which can close to prevent too much water loss.

Page 19

1   Hormones, lower, quickly, upwards.

2   Iris – controls the amount of light entering the eye; retina – acts as the receptor for light (it is sensitive to light); optic nerve – takes information to the brain; lens – focuses the light onto the retina.

Page 21

1 Water, carbon dioxide, water, urea.

2 The sugar level will go up, insulin will be produced (by the pancreas), this lowers the blood sugar level.

Environment

Page 25

1 More light (so more plants, therefore more small animals for the owls to feed on); more small birds (to eat); more plant growth (so more animals for the owls to feed on).

2 There are likely to be fewer (as more owls to eat them).

Page 27

1 Green plants → slugs → blackbirds.

2 a There would be fewer blackbirds unless there was plenty of fruit to eat instead.

b There might be fewer mice because the weasels eat them instead, or there might be more mice as there would be more grass to eat.

Page 29

1 Bacteria, fungi, oxygen, carbon dioxide, decay, respiration.

2 Compost plants and break down sewage.

Page 31

1 Building, rubbish tips, raw materials (e.g. quarrying for stone), farming.

2 Carbon dioxide, nitrogen oxides, sulphur dioxide.

3 By releasing the gases (in question 2) into the atmosphere, they dissolve in rain to form acid rain, the car is burning petrol (a fossil fuel).

Inheritance and Selection

Page 35

1 Nucleus, chromosomes, genes, alleles.

2 They have exactly the same genes (genetic material).

Page 37

1 Warm, wet conditions.

2 Hormones, fertility, pituitary gland, secreted.

Page 39

1 A change in the genes of an organism, caused by radiation and some chemicals.

2 An environmental change (e.g. temperature, amount of rain), predators may eat them all, disease may kill them all, another species successfully competes against them (e.g. eats all of their food).

3 Mutation, evolution, extinction.

Metals

Page 43

1 Oxygen, hydroxide, hydrochloric acid, hydrogen.

2

Metals	Non-metals
shiny when cut	brittle when solid
form alloys	most are gases at room temperature
good conductors of electricity	poor conductors of heat

Page 45

1 Reduce, iron, more, carbon monoxide, calcium carbonate, slag.

Page 47

1 Oxide, cryolite, negative, positive.

2 So that the different ions are free to move to the electrodes.

3 Na, Al, C, Fe, Au (least reactive).

Page 49

1 Potassium sulphate, potassium nitrate, calcium chloride, sodium nitrate.

2 Nitrogen oxides and sulphur dioxide.

Earth Materials

Page 53

1 Some seem to 'fit' well together, fossils are similar on continents hundreds of miles apart, there are similar rocks on continents hundreds of miles apart.

2 They float on the mantle, there are convection currents in the mantle, these are caused by heat produced by radioactive processes.

3 When plates collide one may be forced down, the other is forced up, resulting in mountains.

Page 55

1 From sediment (e.g. sand) building up on the sea floor, the weight squeezes water out, the sediment cements together as salts crystallise out.

2 The magma which formed the rock cooled quickly, it may have cooled on top of the surface of the Earth.

3 If they are placed under great heat and pressure.

Page 57

1 Calcium carbonate, quicklime, slaked lime, cement.

2 If a similar range of fossils is found in two different rocks then the rocks must have been formed at about the same time (this is because the animals and plants present must have lived at about the same time).

3 It is worn away (eroded), the sediment is carried to the sea, sedimentary rock is formed, Earth movements cause the rock to move beneath the crust, it melts and forms magma, it comes back to the surface and forms igneous rock.

Page 59

1 a A   b B   c A.

2 Porous, less dense, non-porous.

3 Because porous rock contains water, oil is less dense and so floats on the water.

Page 61

1 The amount of carbon dioxide is increasing, more of the energy (heat) from the Sun is trapped in the atmosphere and less is reflected back out into space.

2 Nitrogen, oxygen, carbon dioxide, argon.

Patterns of Chemical Change

Page 65

1 The particles bump into each other more often as there are more particles in the same space.

2 Increase, collide, greater.

3 The substances reacting will be used up quicker (solids may disappear more quickly), products (e.g. gases) will be produced more quickly.

Page 67

1 Iron and platinum.

2 At 30°C the enzyme still works, at 45°C the enzyme stops working (the enzyme is damaged by the high temperature).

3 Useful substances would include: alcohol, carbon dioxide and yoghurt.

Page 69

1 To work out the M_r of the compound you need to know the A_r of each element making up the compound:

a $CaCO_3$: Ca = 40, C = 12, O = 16 (but there are three of them, so 48)
$M_r = 40 + 12 + 48 = 100$.

b $MgSO_4$: Mg = 24, S = 32, O = 16 (but there are four of them, so 64)
$M_r = 24 + 32 + 64 = 120$.

2 a The M_r of sodium chloride is: (Na = 23) + (Cl = 35) = 58
therefore the proportion of sodium = $\frac{23}{58}$
= 39.7%.

b The M_r of sulphur dioxide is: (S = 32) + (O = 16, but there are two of them so 32) = 64
therefore the proportion of sulphur = $\frac{32}{64}$
= 50%.

Page 70

1 a Something that will easily catch fire.

b There are many, but petrol is a good answer.

2 Through the skin, breathed in, eaten.

3 a A filter funnel (with filter paper) can be used to separate solids from liquids, a Bunsen burner is used to heat materials.

b Place filter paper in funnel, pour mixture into top, liquid filters through, solids are trapped by paper.

Structures and Bonding

Page 73

1 Liquid, gas, solid.

2 There is always exactly the same number (protons are positive, electrons are negative so the charges are balanced).

Page 75

1 a 12   b 24   c 12   d 2, 8, 2

2

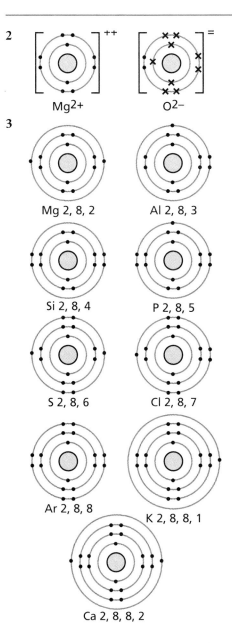

Mg²⁺   O²⁻

3

Mg 2, 8, 2   Al 2, 8, 3

Si 2, 8, 4   P 2, 8, 5

S 2, 8, 6   Cl 2, 8, 7

Ar 2, 8, 8   K 2, 8, 8, 1

Ca 2, 8, 8, 2

Page 77

1 Atoms, sharing, low.

Page 79

1 *Any three from:* are non-metals, have coloured vapour as gases, exist as pairs of atoms (therefore are molecules), form ionic salts (where the halogen carries one negative charge), form molecular compounds with other non-metals.

2 Because the outer (highest energy) shell of electrons is already full.

3 As it loses one electron to become an ion – it therefore now has one more proton (positive charge) in the nucleus than electrons (negative charge) in the electron shells.

Page 81

1 Chloride, positive, electron, chlorine.

2 In photographic film and photographic paper.

3 The spider should have: chlorine, hydrogen and sodium hydroxide.

Page 83

1 a NaOH   b MgO   c Na_2O d $MgCl_2$.

2 a Magnesium + oxygen produces magnesium oxide.

  b Potassium + water produces potassium hydroxide and hydrogen.

  c Sodium + chlorine produces sodium chloride.

Energy

Page 87

1 Conduction, radiation, insulation, convection.

2 This colour does not absorb much radiation (heat), it reflects it – the people in the car stay cooler.

3 It traps air, which is a good insulator.

Page 89

1 The spider diagram should include at least *three* appliances, e.g. radio, television, CD player, Walkman.

2 Power $= \dfrac{\text{energy transferred}}{\text{time}}$

$= \dfrac{6000}{8}$

$= 750\,\text{W(atts)}$

Page 91

1 Non-renewable sources could include: nuclear, coal, oil, gas.
Renewable sources could include: wind, tidal, hydroelectric, solar and wood.

2 *Two* advantages might be that the source is renewable and doesn't produce chemical pollution.
Two disadvantages might be that they spoil the countryside and are noisy.

Electricity

Page 95

1 a X = resistor b Y = lamp c 4 A d 6 V e 3 V

2 Cell, adding, components.

Page 97

1 Power = $\dfrac{\text{potential}}{\text{difference}} \times \dfrac{\text{current}}{\text{(amps)}}$
$\qquad\quad$ (volts)
$\qquad = \ 230 \times 5$
$\qquad = \ 1150 \, \text{W(atts)}$

2 Volts, watts, amperes.

Page 99

1 Neutral is blue, earth is green/yellow, brown is live.

2 Rub, charge, positively, negatively.

Page 101

1 Circuit breakers work more quickly and are reset more easily.

2 Increase the strength of the magnetic field, increase the amount of current flowing through the wire.

3 Increase the strength of the current, increase the number of turns on the coil, place an iron core inside the coil.

Page 103

1 Battery, current, magnets, momentum.

2 **B**, the cone vibrating

3 Because you need a very large current, you need thick wires to carry a very large current, it would be expensive to have these thick wires all of the way from the ignition to the starter motor.

Page 105

1 Move the coil of wire faster, make the magnetic field stronger, have more turns on the coil of wire.

2 Rotated, magnetic field, lines of force, potential difference.

3 To alter the voltage.

Forces

Page 109

1 Speed $= \dfrac{\text{distance}}{\text{time}}$
$\qquad\quad = \dfrac{5000}{200}$
$\qquad\quad = 25 \text{ m/s}$

2 Acceleration $= \dfrac{\text{change in velocity}}{\text{time}}$
$\qquad\qquad\ = \dfrac{56 - 0}{8} \ \text{ or } \ \dfrac{56}{8}$
$\qquad\qquad\ = \ 7 \text{ m/s}^2$

3 Steady (constant) acceleration, then constant velocity, then constant deceleration (or negative acceleration), then stops.

Page 111

1 Because the downward force of the boat is balanced by the upward force of the water. It floats lower in the water because it is heavier so its downward force is increased.

2 If your mass is 60 kg you weigh about 600 N (you multiply your mass by 10).

3 a The forward force is greater than the backward (opposite) force.

  b The backward (or opposite) force is greater than the forward force.

Page 113

1 Because the parachute offers much greater resistance against the force of gravity (this means it is much more difficult to pull down through the air).

2 Things which might cause a car to slow down more slowly include: the driver's reaction time, poor road conditions (e.g. icy or wet), the tyres are worn and haven't much tread left to grip the road.

3 The force of gravity and the force of friction through the air.

Page 115

1 Work done = force × distance, therefore the work done = 200 × 450 = 90 000 J (90 kJ).

2 The lorry because although it is travelling at the same speed it is much heavier.

3 He will end up in the river as the elastic will stretch too far, the person jumping will not spring back up.

Page 117

1 Pressure $= \dfrac{\text{force}}{\text{area}}$
$\qquad\qquad = \dfrac{1200}{0.05}$
$\qquad\qquad = 24\,000 \text{ N/m}^2$

2 Because it can go deeper into the sea, the pressure of water increases with its depth.

3 Force, master, pressure, slave, bigger.

Page 119

1 A balance between its high speed (which would cause it to fly off into space) and the force of gravity (which would cause it to fall to Earth).

2 The light does not have to pass through our atmosphere, it only goes through space so there is no interference.

3 They reflect light from our Sun.

Waves and Radiation

Page 121

1 a D b A c B.

Page 123

1 Reflected, refracted, reflected, refracted.

2
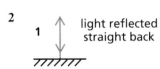
light reflected straight back

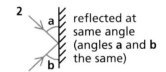
reflected at same angle (angles **a** and **b** the same)

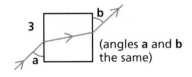
(angles **a** and **b** the same)

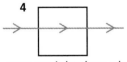
goes straight through

Page 125

1 Microwaves, ultraviolet, X-rays, gamma.

2 All types of electromagnetic radiation can pass through space (a vacuum). *Sound is not a type of electromagnetic radiation.*

Page 127

1 TV controls – infrared; transmit information – radio waves; sun beds – ultraviolet; fracture pictures – X-rays.

2 They pass through soft material but not bones – they therefore make 'shadow' pictures.

3 There are many examples but one choice might be gamma rays – this type of radiation can cause cancers, on the other hand the rays can be targeted to kill cancer cells.

Page 129

1 Because it will go through a great thickness of paper.

2 Gamma, alpha, beta, background.

3 Uses might include: UV and sun beds, infrared and heaters, microwaves and cooking food, gamma rays and killing harmful bacteria in food, X-rays and taking pictures of fractures – there are many!

Index

A

abdomen 6
acceleration
  formulae 109
  speed and velocity 108–9
acids
  acid-alkali reactions 49
  pH scale 48
acid rain 31, 61
activation energy 65
aerobic respiration 6
air sacs *see* alveoli
alcohol 21, 67
alkali metals 78
alkalinity
  neutralisation 49, 83
  pH scale 48
alleles 34
alloys 42
alpha particles 128
alternating current 105
aluminium
  extraction, by electrolysis 46–7
  reactivity 43
  uses 42
alveoli 7
  gas exchange 7
amino acids 5
ammeter 96
ammonium nitrate, Haber process 66
amperes (A) 96
amplitude (wave) 121
anaerobic respiration 6
animal cell 14–15
antibodies/antitoxins 11
anus 4, 5
apparatus, chemical 70
argon (Ar) 61, 79
arteries 9
asexual reproduction 35
atmosphere, Earth's 60–1
atomic mass, relative 68, 77
atomic number 74
atomic structure 129, 130
atoms
  history 130
  mass number 73
  theory 76
atrium 8

B

background radiation 128
bacteria 10, 28, 67, 81
  see also microbes
balance 19
battery 94, 105
beta particles 128
biomass pyramid 27
birth control 37
blast furnace 44–5
blood 8–9, 20–1
blood circulation system 8–9
blood vessels, types 9
body temperature,
  thermoregulatory centre 20
boiling point 72
bonds
  covalent 75–6
  ionic 75, 80, 82–3, 95
brakes, force multipliers 117
braking distance 113
breathing and respiration 6–7
breeding, selective 36
bronchiole 7
bronchus 7
burning *see* combustion

C

calcium 43
calcium carbonate 45, 56
calcium hydroxide 56
calcium oxide 56
cancer cells 127–8
capillaries 9
car
  acceleration 110
  hydraulic systems 117
  pollution caused 31
  starter motor 103
  stopping distance 113
carbohydrases 5
carbohydrates 3, 5
carbon 47
carbon cycle 29
carbon dioxide 15, 20, 45, 67
  in blood 9
  carbon cycle 29
  combustion of fuels 31, 60
  greenhouse effect 60
  from respiration 7
  test 70
carbon monoxide, blast furnace 45
carrier, gene 34
catalysts/catalysis 64–6
cathode 46
cell membrane 2, 9, 14
cell wall 14
cells 2, 8, 14–15
cement 56

chemical bonds 75–7
chemical calculations 68–9
chemical equations 83
chemical formulae 82
chemical reactions *see* reactions
chemical structures, and bonding
  72–83
chemical symbols 82
chlorine 42
chlorine gas test 70
chlorophyll/chloroplasts 14–15
cholera 11
chromosomes 34–5
circuit
  electrical 94–5
  in parallel 94
  in series 94
  symbols 95
circuit breakers 100
circulatory system 8–9
cloning 35, 36
combustion 60
community
  definition 25
  stability 25, 28
competition 24
compounds 75–6
  chemical formulae 48–9, 68–9
  covalent 75–6
  ionic 75, 80, 82–3, 95
  metals/non-metals 48–9
  properties 48–9
  reactions *see* reactions
  relative formula mass 68–9
concrete 56
conduction 86
conductors 42, 86, 98
constellation 119
continental drift 52
contraception 37
convection 86
coordination 18–19
copper, uses 42
copper purification 47
cornea 19
covalent bonds/compounds 75–6
cryolite 46
current
  alternating (a.c.) 105
  direct (d.c.) 105
  measurement 96
current-voltage graphs 97
cystic fibrosis 34
cytoplasm 2, 14